THE WORST WITCH

Adapted from Jill Murphy's original books

by Emma Reeves

With music by Luke Potter

samuelfrench.co.uk

ISBN 978-0-573-11629-2

www.samuelfrench.co.uk

www.samuelfrench.com

THINKING ABOUT PERFORMING A SHOW?

There are thousands of plays and musicals available to perform from Samuel French right now, and applying for a licence is easier and more affordable than you might think

From classic plays to brand new musicals, from monologues to epic dramas, there are shows for everyone.

Plays and musicals are protected by copyright law, so if you want to perform them, the first thing you'll need is a licence. This simple process helps support the playwright by ensuring they get paid for their work and means that you'll have the documents you need to stage the show in public.

Not all our shows are available to perform all the time, so it's important to check and apply for a licence before you start rehearsals or commit to doing the show.

LEARN MORE & FIND THOUSANDS OF SHOWS

Browse our full range of plays and musicals, and find out more about how to license a show

www.samuelfrench.co.uk/perform

Talk to the friendly experts in our Licensing team for advice on choosing a show and help with licensing

plays@samuelfrench.co.uk   020 7387 9373

Acting Editions

BORN TO PERFORM

Playscripts designed from the ground up to work the way you do in rehearsal, performance and study

---

Larger, clearer text for easier reading

Wider margins for notes

Performance features such as character and props lists, sound and lighting cues, and more

---

+ CHOOSE A SIZE AND STYLE TO SUIT YOU

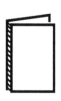

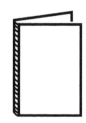

STANDARD EDITION

Our regular paperback book at our regular size

SPIRAL-BOUND EDITION

The same size as the Standard Edition, but with a sturdy, easy-to-fold, easy-to-hold spiral-bound spine

LARGE EDITION

A4 size and spiral bound, with larger text and a blank page for notes opposite every page of text – perfect for technical and directing use

LEARN MORE   samuelfrench.co.uk/actingeditions

MUSIC USE NOTE

The music parts for this title are available on hire to licensed productions from Samuel French. Fees and conditions of this hire are quoted on application.

Sample materials are available on request for perusal prior to application.

USE OF COPYRIGHT MUSIC

A licence issued by Samuel French Ltd to perform this play does not include permission to use the incidental music specified in this copy.

Where the place of performance is already licensed by the PERFORMING RIGHT SOCIETY (PRS) a return of the music used must be made to them. If the place of performance is not so licensed then application should be made to the PRS, 2 Pancras Square, London, N1C 4AG.

A separate and additional licence from PHONOGRAPHIC PERFORMANCE LTD, 1 Upper James Street, London W1F 9DE (www.ppluk.com) is needed whenever commercial recordings are used.

IMPORTANT BILLING AND CREDIT REQUIREMENTS

If you have obtained performance rights to this title, please refer to your licensing agreement for important billing and credit requirements.

ABOUT THE AUTHOR

Jill Murphy was born in London and attended the Ursuline Convent in Wimbledon which, together with the boarding school stories she enjoyed reading, provided much of the material and inspiration for *The Worst Witch* – started in her school rough book, aged fourteen.

Mildred Hubble is very much a self-portrait. Jill put the book on hold while she attended both Chelsea and Croydon Art Schools, but continued to write it while living in a village in West Africa for two years and then while working as a nanny back at home. The book was published when Jill was twenty-four and proved an instant success.

Jill continued working as a nanny, until the publication of *The Worst Witch Strikes Again* prompted her to devote herself to full-time writing and illustration. The Worst Witch stories have become some of the most outstandingly successful titles on the Puffin paperback list and have sold more than five million copies. There are now eight Worst Witch titles. *The Worst Witch* was also made into a television series for ITV in the early 1990s and there is currently a major television series with CBBC.

Jill is also well known for her picture books. She was commended for the 1980 Kate Greenaway Medal for *Peace at Last*. *Five Minutes' Peace*, the first in her series about the Large Family (of elephants), won the 1987 Parents Magazine Best Books for Babies Award, as well as being shortlisted for the 1986 Children's Book Award. From the same series, *All in One Piece* was highly commended for the 1987 Kate Greenaway Award and shortlisted for the 1987 Children's Book Award, and *A Quiet Night In* was shortlisted for the Kate Greenaway Medal in 1994. *The Last Noo-Noo* won the 0–5 category of the 1995 Smarties Book Prize and in the same year was shortlisted for the English 4–11 Outstanding Children's Book of the Year, going on to win the 1996 Sheffield Children's Book Award. *The Last Noo-Noo* won the 1996 Gateshead Gold Award and in the same year was adapted as a play and performed at the Polka Theatre, London.

Jill lives in Cornwall and has a grown-up son, named Charlie.

ABOUT THE ADAPTOR

Emma Reeves is from Wrexham in North Wales. She has written West End adaptations of Jacqueline Wilson's *Hetty Feather* (Olivier-nominated and CAMEO Award winner), *Carrie's War*, *Little Women* and *Cool Hand Luke*. Other stage work includes: *Anne of Green Gables*, *The Ugly Duckling* and *The Snow Child*. TV credits include: *The Worst Witch* (lead writer), *Eve* (lead writer, co-creator), *The Dumping Ground*, *Young Dracula*, *The Story of Tracy Beaker*, *Hetty Feather*, *Spirit Warriors*, *Belonging*, *Doctors* and *The Murder of Princess Diana* (Lifetime Channel). Audio work includes: plays for Radio 4, Radio Wales and Big Finish (including original *Doctor Who* and *Torchwood* stories). Emma has won Best Children's TV Episode at The Writers' Guild Awards twice. Other awards include an RTS Best Children's Drama (*Tracy Beaker Returns*), RTS North East award for Best Children's Programme (*The Dumping Ground*) and RTS Scotland Award for Best Children's Drama (*Eve*). In October 2016 two of Emma's episodes from *The Dumping Ground* and *Hetty Feather* were nominated for a Children's BAFTA for Best Drama. Her episodes of both *Eve* and *Hetty Feather* have been nominated for the Broadcast Award for Best Children's Programme.

ADAPTOR'S NOTE

I grew up with Jill Murphy's Worst Witch books – well, some of them. Only the first three had been published when I was a child, and I read them over and over again. As an adult I was delighted to work with Jill, first on a television adaptation of the books, and then on this new play.

Jill began writing *The Worst Witch* when she was still one of the few working-class students at a strict and somewhat snobbish Catholic grammar school. She excelled at writing and drawing, but the nuns who ran the school always made her feel that she didn't really belong. As Jill sought refuge in her imagination, transforming the everyday joys and miseries of childhood into something magical, the nuns who taught and tormented her became Miss Hardbroom and her coven of teacher-witches. Jill's school friends and rivals were transformed into Maud, Enid and Ethel. And Jill herself – a bright, well-intentioned but unlucky, accident-prone girl with a tendency to daydream – became Mildred Hubble.

Like her creator, Mildred is an outsider who is made to feel that she will never be good enough. Many people feel like that. Especially young people. Especially girls.

There are now eight Worst Witch books. I am sure many of those who read, perform in or watch this play will have read some or all of them. They might also have seen one or more of the television and film adaptations – perhaps even the one I worked on! And so, in creating the stage show, we aimed to do something a little different. Something that would celebrate the unique connection between performers and audience offered by live theatre. We decided to bring the world of Miss Cackle's Academy into a contemporary theatre, as Mildred and her friends put on a play about life at witching school. A show written by and starring the "worst witch in the whole school" – what can possibly go wrong?

To me, the heart of the Worst Witch series lies in the deep connection between Jill and her material. Mildred's misadventures are very funny, but there's also something heartbreaking about an eleven-year-old girl who's been constantly told that she's the "worst". I don't think the messages we receive about ourselves in childhood can ever be entirely deleted, whether you're an entitled Ethel or an underdog like Mildred. But the message of *The Worst Witch* is eternally optimistic. Kindness, loyalty and bravery will be rewarded in the end – as long as you never give up.

I hope this play will send a message of support to the Mildred Hubble in all of us. May we all be inspired and encouraged – and never let anybody tell us we'll never be good enough.

Emma Reeves, January 2019

ROYAL & DERNGATE NORTHAMPTON

Chief Executive Jo Gordon
Artistic Director James Dacre

Royal & Derngate is the main venue for arts and entertainment in Northamptonshire, with audience members for live shows and films numbering 378,000 last year, and an additional 115,000 seeing its work on tour at over eighty-five venues. Named Regional Theatre of the Year in The Stage Awards in 2011 (and nominated again in 2016), the theatre won the UK Theatre Awards for Best Presentation of Touring Theatre in 2015 and Best Touring Production in 2016 for *The Herbal Bed*, and The Stage Ensemble Award and a Fringe First for *Education, Education, Education* in 2017.

Alongside touring nationally and internationally, Royal & Derngate's Made in Northampton productions have transferred to the West End and Broadway as well as Shakespeare's Globe, the National Theatre, Hackney Empire and the Lyric Hammersmith. The venue also presents a diverse range of visiting productions on both the Derngate and Royal stages, featuring musicals, dance, comedy and music, including a residency from the Royal Philharmonic Orchestra.

Royal & Derngate's award-winning, nationally recognised Get Involved programme engages with over 21,000 participants each year, including schools, families and communities in Northamptonshire and beyond, and its two-screen cinema welcomed over 82,000 audience members to the best in world, independent, British and mainstream film. Meanwhile, the theatre's Generate artistic development programme supports hundreds of local and emerging artists and practitioners each year.

Royal & Derngate also continues to work in partnership to manage The Core at Corby Cube.

F /royalandderngate
T @royalderngate

Box Office 01604 624811
www.royalandderngate.co.uk

The Worst Witch was first produced at the Royal & Derngate Northampton, (James Dacre, Artistic Director; Jo Gordon, Chief Executive), as a Royal & Derngate Northampton, Kenny Wax Family Entertainment, Novel Theatre and Nica Burns Co-Production, on 27 November 2018, with the following cast and creatives:

Ethel	Rosie Abraham
Mildred	Danielle Bird
Enid	Anna Crichlow
Miss Bat/Piano/Guitar/Cello	Molly-Grace Cutler
Fenella/Bass Guitar	Meg Forgan
Miss Hardbroom	Rachel Heaton
Maud	Rebecca Killick
Drusilla	Emma Lau
Miss Drill/Guitar/Drums/Percussion/Clarinet	Megan Leigh Mason
Agatha/Miss Cackle	Polly Lister

Adaptor	Emma Reeves
Author	Jill Murphy
Director	Theresa Heskins
Designer	Simon Daw
Composer	Luke Potter
Movement Director	Beverley Norris-Edmunds
Lighting Designer	Aideen Malone
Sound Designer	Leigh Davies
Aerial Consultant	Vicki Amedume
Magic Consultant	John Bulleid
Puppetry Designer and Director	Paschale Straiton
Casting Director	Anji Carroll CDG
Associate Director	Ellie Taylor
Associate Sound Designer	Rory Maguire
Vocal Coach	Laura Bowler
Video Production	Simon Beckett for Factotum Film
Assistant Director	Sarah Stacey

Company Stage Manager on the Book	Fiona McCulloch
Technical Stage Manager	Will Hunter
Sound Operator	James Scotney
Wardrobe Manager	Shermaine "T" Gocoul
Wardrobe Assistant	Ellen Murgatroyd
Tech Swing	Dhiren Basu

Scenery, set painting, properties, costuming, wigs and make-up by Royal & Derngate workshops and facilitated in-house by stage management and technical teams.

Royal & Derngate Team

Senior Producer	Rosie Townshend
Consultant Producer Peter Huntley for Smart Entertainment
Producer	Tess Dowdeswell
Head of Production	Martin Thompson
Technical Manager	Mark Lowe
Senior Technician (Stage)	Matt Revell
Head of Lighting & Sound	Liam Matthews
Senior Technician (Sound/Lighting)	Andy Cox
Technicians	Jonathan Blunsdon, Chris Rice
Head of Wardrobe	Victoria Youngson
Deputy Head of Wardrobe	Felicity Jones
Wardrobe Assistant	Louise Smith
Head of Scenic Art	Jen Hallas Riddick
Head of Workshop	Paul Beasley
Deputy Head of Workshop	Ross White
Carpenter/Propmaker	Kieran Shyrane
Company Stage Manager	Sara Crathorne
Assistant Stage Manager	Darren Abel

A special thank you to all the people who contributed to the development of the project through the R&D process: Nick Ash, James Atherton, Hannah Edwards, Barbara Hockaday, Caroline Horton, Francesca Mills, Emma Palliant, Charlotte Miranda Smith.

To Jill, with thanks for many years of magic

CHARACTERS

MISS ADA CACKLE
MISS HECATE HARDBROOM
MISS BAT
MISS DRILL
MILDRED HUBBLE
MAUD SPELLBODY
ENID NIGHTSHADE
ETHEL HALLOW
DRUSILLA PADDOCK
FENELLA FEVERFEW
AGATHA CACKLE
TABBY

Pre-Show

The students and teachers mingle with the audience, talking about the play they're about to perform about life at Miss Cackle's Academy. **MILDRED, MAUD** *and* **ENID** *are really excited to be here, to tell stories about their lives and let other kids know about opportunities in witching.* **ETHEL** *is snooty about mixing with "plebs", "oiks", "riff-raff", "rabble" and "basics".* **MISS HARDBROOM** *keeps a sharp eye on proceedings, discouraging too much familiarity between student witches and audience members and moving the* **GIRLS** *on if they've chatted too long with one group.*

ACT ONE

Prologue

MISS HARDBROOM urges silence as MISS CACKLE takes the stage. MAUD rushes backstage, frantically yelling instructions to unseen crew on cans. As the GIRLS take their opening positions, MILDRED has an attack of stage fright, ENID tries to calm her down and get her to breathe.

MISS CACKLE Good evening [afternoon / morning as appropriate] and welcome to our little show... Mildred, is everything quite all right?

ENID Yeah, she's cool. Just a bit of stage fright.

MILDRED I think I'm going to be sick.

MISS CACKLE *(calm)* Use the cauldron, stage left. No, your other left, dear.

MILDRED zig-zags crazily across the stage and vanishes into the wings. ENID shrugs and follows. ETHEL runs up to MISS CACKLE.

ETHEL Miss Cackle, poor Mildred's not well. I think we should cancel the show.

MISS CACKLE Ethel, that's very thoughtful of you. And quite, quite wrong. What is the first rule of witchcraft?

ETHEL A witch does what must be done.

MISS CACKLE And, co-incidentally, the first rule of "showbiz" is, the show must go on!

MAUD and ENID appear, supporting a jelly-legged MILDRED.

MAUD She's absolutely fine, Miss Cackle!

MILDRED *waves weakly. They carry her off again.*

MISS CACKLE There, you see! Nothing wrong with her that "Doctor Theatre" won't cure.

To the audience.

I'm sure you understand why the girls are nervous. They've been busy all term, writing and rehearsing their play. I've never seen them work so hard.

MISS HARDBROOM *appears.*

MISS HARDBROOM I've never seen some of them work at all.

MISS CACKLE Ah, Miss Hardbroom.

To the audience.

My invaluable Deputy Head. Who has kindly agreed to appear in the show tonight!

MISS HARDBROOM Reluctantly. But I could hardly allow the girls to fool around impersonating senior witches.

ENID *(enters)* I really wanted to play you!

Does a **MISS HARDBROOM** *face / pose.*

MISS HARDBROOM Exactly. As I could not prevent this entertainment, I did what I could to mitigate the disaster. The use of magic is banned entirely from the proceedings.

MISS CACKLE Quite right. We can't be throwing spells around in a theatre. Utterly irresponsible.

MISS HARDBROOM We'll leave that sort of thing to the wizards. I also insisted that all cats were left at the school. I felt it was my duty to protect the poor, innocent animals. The rest of you have only yourselves to blame. Right, I suppose we'd better get on with it.

MISS CACKLE Ooh, I'm getting chills.

To the audience.

Tonight [or today], we are making history. Our beloved Academy is the oldest magical school in Britain – the original, you might say. And for the first time, here at...

MISS CACKLE *looks at* **MISS DRILL,** *who provides the name of the theatre where the show is taking place.*

[name of theatre] Thank you! We are casting the veil aside and sharing just a few of our witching secrets with the, er...the...

MISS HARDBROOM ...Plebs...

MISS CACKLE ...Wonderfully diverse talent of tomorrow. So, if my girls' play inspires you to seek a witching education, you know where to find us! At the very top of the mountain, just past the Spooky Forest and the Mystery Mists. Got that? Good. And now—

MISS CACKLE *produces a crumpled piece of paper and squints through her glasses as she reads:*

Miss Cackle's Academy presents – "The Worst Witch", by Mildred Hubble! Executive Producer, Enid Nightshade.

ETHEL *marches onto the stage, annoyed.*

ETHEL Executive Producer? What does that even mean?

ENID *confronts her.*

ENID My parents paid for all this, so get off until it's your bit.

ETHEL You can't tell me what to do.

MAUD, *with cans, runs on and drags them off.*

MAUD Stop it, you two! And get backstage! – Sorry, Miss Cackle.

MISS CACKLE *(continues unfazed)* With direction, stage management, costumes and props by Maud Spellbody. I hope you enjoy it as much as the girls have!

MISS CACKLE *leaves. The play begins.*

The Foot of the Mountain

The GIRLS *are waiting at the foot of the mountain with suitcases and cat baskets.* MILDRED *rides towards them on a scooter. She's wearing the wrong school tie. She can't control the scooter. She veers around and almost crashes into the group of* GIRLS, *who yell – "Watch out! Look where you're going!" etc.*

MILDRED Look out!

> MILDRED *eventually crashes into* MAUD *and they end up tangled in a heap.*

Sorry – sorry!

> MAUD *helps* MILDRED *up.*

MAUD Is that a real scooter? I've never seen one before.

ETHEL Apparently, neither has she.

> DRUSILLA *laughs sycophantically.*

MILDRED It's new. I'm not very good yet.

DRUSILLA We know. 'Cos it looks like you've never been on one before.

ETHEL *(sotto, irritated)* Yes, that's basically what I just said.

MAUD Ignore them. Hi, I'm Maud Spellbody.

MILDRED Mildred Hubble.

MAUD Are you waiting for the Academy transport?

MILDRED Is there a bus? I was just going to scoot.

MAUD You can't scoot all the way there! Just wait here with us.

ETHEL *You're* going to the Academy? Are you *sure*?

MILDRED Yes. I got my place months ago.

MAUD Of course she is. Or she wouldn't be able to see us.

MILDRED What d'you mean?

MAUD They told us there would be protective spells at the meeting place.

MILDRED *Spells?*

ETHEL Yes, spells. Mummy warned me that standards are slipping.

MAUD *(to* **MILDRED***)* Don't worry, we're not all like her.

Magical music.

Look!

MAUD *points as a graceful flight of witches takes to the sky above the* **GIRLS***.*

MILDRED What's that?

MAUD The older girls, flying on their broomsticks. But one day, that will be us...

ETHEL *(looks up critically)* I hope not. Look at that one's posture! She's like a crooked old hag. *I* got full marks for posture in my Broomstick Proficiency.

DRUSILLA Amazing. I'm Drusilla by the way.

ETHEL Ethel Hallow. Yes, one of *the* Hallows.

DRUSILLA So your sisters—

ETHEL – Have all been Head Girls, yes.

MILDRED *(to* **MAUD***)* You know, I'm pretty sure I shouldn't be here.

MAUD That's just first day nerves. Everyone feels like that sometimes.

FENELLA *and* **DRUSILLA** *are taking selfies with* **ETHEL***.*

ETHEL *(boasting to* **DRUSILLA***)* ...And I've done Grade Five Cauldron and Grade Six magical gesticulation...

MAUD *(makes a face)* Except her. Don't worry. You'll be fine.

MILDRED Will I?

(pinches herself) Ow!

MAUD What did you do that for?

MILDRED I'm trying to wake up. 'Cos this has got to be a dream.

MAUD You're panicking. Calm down. Breathe.

MILDRED *(in danger of hyperventilating)* Spells. Flying on broomsticks. Things like this don't happen in real life.

MAUD Didn't you read the prospectus?

MILDRED Loads of times! I brought it with me.

> **MILDRED** *digs out a battered prospectus for City Road Academy.*

MAUD *(encouraging)* There you are, you see? Everything's fine. You're totally meant to be here at—

> **MILDRED** *hands the prospectus to* **MAUD***, who reads...*

...City Road Academy...oh. I see what you mean. Yes, you're totally in the wrong place.

MILDRED So where *am* I?

> **MISS HARDBROOM** *appears.*

MISS HARDBROOM Well met, girls.

GIRLS *(except* **MILDRED***)* Well met, Miss Hardbroom.

MISS HARDBROOM I trust you all remembered to bring your kittens.

GIRLS *(except* **MILDRED***)* Yes, Miss Hardbroom.

The GIRLS *open their cat baskets to produce puppet cats.*

MISS HARDBROOM *(to* MILDRED*)* You! Where is your familiar?

MILDRED What's a familiar?

ETHEL A familiar is a key tool of the witching craft.

MAUD *(sotto) You're* a key tool of the witching craft.

ETHEL Useful for assistance with potions and flying – and of course, remote viewing. Once a witch has truly bonded with her cat, she will be able to see through his eyes.

MILDRED *(now desperate to get away)* Um – Miss – I really don't think I—

MISS HARDBROOM The instructions were very clear. One kitten per girl. No frogs, toads, hares, cockerels, bats or badgers – oh no, don't tell me you've brought an *owl*?

MILDRED Why would I bring an owl?

MISS HARDBROOM Because *some* young witches think the rules don't apply to them. I blame the parents. They've bred a generation who lack discipline and self-control... They are... oh, what is the modern parlance? Soft, flaky and liable to melt into a puddle—

ETHEL Snowflakes, Miss Hardbroom.

MISS HARDBROOM Snowflakes. Thank you...

Looks ETHEL *up and down, taking in her confidence.*

...I assume I am addressing the youngest Hallow sister?

ETHEL My name's Ethel. And by the time I leave, I'll be the only Hallow you remember.

MISS HARDBROOM *(making mental notes)* Arrogant. Competitive. Ruthless. You have the potential to become a fine witch. And don't you just know it. As for the rest of you...

(looks them over) Never mind. Prepare for Transportation.

The other GIRLS *pick up their luggage.* MILDRED *looks around.*

MILDRED Is the bus coming? I don't see it.

The other GIRLS *are puzzled by this, but there's little time to react as* MISS HARDBROOM *makes a magical gesture...*

Miss Cackle's Academy

...And the scene changes around them as the Main School Set is revealed. MISS CACKLE *enters and joins* MISS HARDBROOM. *The* GIRLS *gaze around them in awe. Except* MILDRED, *who staggers, on the verge of passing out.* MAUD *holds her up.*

MILDRED *(woozy, confused)* Where am I?

MISS CACKLE Well met, girls. And welcome to Miss Cackle's Academy for Witches...

MILDRED Witches...

MISS CACKLE Are you all right dear?

MAUD It's just the Transportation spell. I don't think she was expecting it.

MISS CACKLE Didn't your mother warn you, child?

MILDRED *shakes her head – no!*

MISS HARDBROOM Hardly surprising! Look at the state of her.

The uniform's all wrong, and she hasn't even brought a familiar—

MILDRED *(terrified of* MISS HARDBROOM*)* I'm sorry! I didn't know!

MISS CACKLE *comes to the rescue.*

MISS CACKLE Not to worry, dear, we've plenty of spare uniforms. And I'm sure we can rustle up a kitten from somewhere.

To everyone.

Now, let's get this show on the road! Take it away, Miss Bat!

MISS BAT, *on piano, nods and launches into the song. During this number, the* GIRLS *are inducted into the witching life, receiving their hats, cloaks, broomsticks and books and* **MILDRED** *changes into a Miss Cackle's Academy uniform.*

MISS CACKLE AND CAST *(sing)*
ONWARD, EVER STRIVING ONWARD
PROUDLY ON OUR BROOMS WE FLY
STRAIGHT AND TRUE ABOVE THE TREE TOPS
SHADOWS ON THE MOONLIT SKY.
NEVER A DAY WILL PASS BEFORE US
WHEN WE HAVEN'T TRIED OUR BEST
KEPT OUR CAULDRONS BUBBLING NICELY
CAST OUR SPELLS AND CHARMS WITH ZEST.

OOOH... DON'T YOU KNOW THAT WE'RE THE WITCHING KIND?
OOOH... DON'T YOU KNOW THAT WE'RE THE WITCHING KIND?

MISS CACKLE *hands out sashes.*

MISS CACKLE These are your House sashes. Yellow for Toadflax –

(hands a yellow sash to **MAUD***)*

– green for Pennywort –

(hands a green sash to **FENELLA***)*

– purple for Wolfsbane.

(she hands a purple sash to **ETHEL***)*

DRUSILLA I want to be in Wolfsbane too!

> **MISS CACKLE** *hands* **DRUSILLA** *a purple sash.*
> **MISS HARDBROOM** *tuts at the indulgence.*

MISS CACKLE And red for Poppy.

> **MILDRED** *looks apprehensively at the red sash and at* **ETHEL** *and* **DRUSILLA**.

MILDRED Thank you. Um – which is the evil house?

MISS CACKLE We don't have one, dear. That would be very silly.

MISS CACKLE AND CAST *(sing)*
    FULL OF JOY WE MIX OUR POTIONS
    WORKING BY EACH OTHER'S SIDE.
    WHEN OUR DAYS AT SCHOOL ARE OVER
    LET US THINK OF THEM WITH PRIDE.
    (ALWAYS STRIVING BY EACH OTHER'S SIDE)
    DON'T YOU KNOW THAT WE'RE THE WITCHING KIND?
    (STRAIGHT AND TRUE, PROUD ON OUR BROOMS WE FLY)
    DON'T YOU KNOW THAT WE'RE THE WITCHING KIND?

    MISS CACKLE *hands out books.*

MISS CACKLE Two books each, girls. *The Book of Common Spells*, and *The Witches' Code*. The sacred binding rules of the Craft. Write your names in the front so you don't lose them.

The **GIRLS** *hold their books reverently and write their names.* **ETHEL** *"accidentally" trips* **MILDRED**, *who drops hers. Pages fly out of the ancient tome and she chases them around the stage.* **MAUD** *helps her.* **MISS HARDBROOM** *picks up the front page and hands it to her, icily.*

MISS HARDBROOM Yours, I presume...

Reading the name.

Mildred Hubble?

MILDRED *nods nervously, takes the page and reassembles the book as best she can.* **MISS CACKLE** *brings* **TABBY** *to* **MILDRED**.

MISS CACKLE Look what Miss Tapioca found in the kitchens! Sorry he's not black.

MILDRED That's OK. I think he's beautiful.

MISS CACKLE *hands* **TABBY** *to* **MILDRED**. **TABBY** *snuggles* **MILDRED** *and purrs.*

MISS CACKLE I think he likes you!

MILDRED I love him! I'll call him Tabby!

MISS CACKLE AND CAST *(sing)*
> WITCHING KIND WE ARE.
> DOUBLE DOUBLE TOIL AND TROUBLE
> FIRE BURN AND CAULDRON BUBBLE
> FILLET OF A FENNY SNAKE
> IN THE CAULDRON BOIL AND BAKE
> EYE OF NEWT AND TOE OF FROG
> WOOL OF BAT AND TONGUE OF DOG
> ADDER'S FORK AND BLIND-WORM'S STING
> LIZARD'S LEG AND HOWLET'S WING
> FOR A CHARM OF POWERFUL TROUBLE
> LIKE A HELL-BROTH BOIL AND BUBBLE
> DOUBLE DOUBLE TOIL AND TROUBLE
> FIRE BURN AND CAULDRON—

ENID *grabs a mic from the* **BAND** *corner.*

ENID What up Northampton! Hey, can I get a what up?

[Maybe she does, maybe she doesn't...]

Time to meet our music coven. On lead guitar, Miss Drill! Our totally witching Head of Sports. Rides a mean broomstick and plays a sick axe riff.

MISS DRILL *demonstrates with a solo.*

Miss Bat in the house!

MISS BAT *looks startled – she was playing piano on autopilot, almost asleep.*

Best Chanting teacher in the biz. Miss Bat's been at this school since Beethoven was a boy.

MISS BAT Who, dear?

ENID *(loudly)* BEETHOVEN.

MISS BAT Sorry, I don't keep up with all this modern music...

ENID *(leading applause)* Give it up for Miss Bat on keys!

MISS BAT *plays a surprisingly cool piano solo.*

And proving that it's all about that bass – Fenella Feverfew!

FENELLA *plays her bass solo.*

ETHEL *gets fed up of* ENID *hogging attention. She grabs the mic:*

ETHEL Enid, you're not even in the story yet. Just stand at the back and shut up.

ENID *You* stand at the back and shut up.

MAUD BOTH of you stand at the back and shut up! This is Mildred's play and you're not going to ruin it!

Realising the audience has heard their squabble, they slink back to their places and continue the song, which builds to a climax:

MISS CACKLE AND CAST *(sing)*
WE'RE THE WITCHING KIND!
DON'T YOU KNOW WE'RE THE WITCHING KIND?
DON'T YOU KNOW, DON'T YOU KNOW WE'RE THE WITCHING
    KIND?
DON'T YOU KNOW WE'RE THE WITCHING KIND?
DON'T YOU KNOW, DON'T YOU KNOW WE'RE THE WITCHING
    KIND?
DON'T YOU KNOW WE'RE THE WITCHING KIND?
DON'T YOU KNOW, DON'T YOU KNOW WE'RE THE WITCHING
    KIND?
DON'T YOU KNOW WE'RE THE WITCHING KIND?

The song ends with a joyful crescendo. The gang catch their breath.

MISS CACKLE Marvellous. Most invigorating.

MISS HARDBROOM Now that you've got that out of your systems, we will proceed to the Potions Lab for your first lesson.

ETHEL *leads the way confidently.* DRUSILLA *and* FENELLA *follow.* MAUD *gestures to* MILDRED *to come with her.* **MILDRED** *shakes her head and tries to sneak off in the other direction, but somehow* **MISS HARDBROOM** *is there before her.*

I take it you have an urgent appointment, Mildred Hubble? Something more important than Double Potions?

MILDRED *shakes her head, terrified.*

Then why are you not following the others?

MILDRED *can't speak.* **MAUD** *comes to her rescue.*

MAUD This way, Millie.

MAUD *grabs* **MILDRED***'s arm, and* **MILDRED** *has no choice but to follow the others to the Potions Lab.*

The Potions Lab

Led by **ETHEL***, the* **GIRLS** *set out witching equipment – cauldrons and ingredients.* **ETHEL** *is the first to notice* **MISS HARDBROOM** *entering. She immediately stops what she's doing and stands straight. The others, including* **MAUD***, copy her.*

MISS HARDBROOM Well met by mornlight, girls.

GIRLS Well met, Miss Hardbroom.

MISS HARDBROOM Open *The Book of Common Spells* at page one. We will begin with the basics. A simple laughter potion—

ETHEL *groans.*

Yes, Ethel?

ETHEL Miss Hardbroom, surely there's no need for *me* to start from the beginning?

MISS HARDBROOM Very well. Ethel Hallow, I give you permission to impress me.

ETHEL I'll brew my signature butterfly levitation potion. When I drink it, I shall flutter around the room with the beauty and grace of a butterfly.

MISS HARDBROOM I'm sure we are all looking forward to that spectacle. The rest of you, get on with your laughter potions.

The **GIRLS** *set to work on their potions – passing around cauldrons and ingredients etc.* **MILDRED** *and* **MAUD** *are working together.* **ETHEL** *works alone.* **DRUSILLA** *works with* **FENELLA***.*

Witchery is all about self-control, discipline and precision. Calculating the perfect ratio is crucial, as is correct measuring and accurate gesticulation. Keep on with your work. I expect you all to achieve an acceptable level of hilarity by lunchtime.

MISS HARDBROOM *goes to another part of the classroom.*

MAUD *(reading from the spell book)* Would you say that was toad green?

MILDRED Close enough.

MILDRED *takes a taste of the potion.* **MAUD** *follows her. They look at each other apprehensively. They don't feel like laughing. They try to force it. Both of them laugh, weakly – then stop.*

(to **MAUD***)* Why isn't it working?

MAUD I don't know. I feel – weird...

MILDRED You mean, like, dizzy? Me too.

MAUD Do my feet look funny to you?

MILDRED I don't know. I can't see them. Why can't I see them?

MILDRED *and* **MAUD** *are slowly becoming invisible. To illustrate this, they cover their bodies with cloth from their feet to their chins.*

MAUD My knees are going.

MILDRED Mine too... What's happening?

Now, only **MILDRED** *and* **MAUD***'s heads are visible.*

MAUD Help! Drusilla!

DRUSILLA *(looking around)* Hello? Who said that?

MILDRED *and* **MAUD** *realise that they are fully invisible.*

FENELLA Sounded like Maud – where is she?

DRUSILLA Mildred's gone too. They're going to get in so much trouble...

MILDRED *and* **MAUD** *try to huddle together and find themselves tangled up awkwardly:*

MILDRED They really can't see us?

MAUD No – ow, that's my foot!

MILDRED That's my arm!

They disentangle themselves.

MAUD What do we do now?

MILDRED This is my chance! I'm not supposed to be here anyway, I can sneak off home—

MAUD You can't go home like that!

MILDRED You're right. My mum'll kill me...

MAUD *looks through The Book of Common Spells.*

MAUD OK, so the laughter potion curdled into an Invisibility Elixir. We just need to stablise it with a bit more pondweed-gathered-at-midnight—

MILDRED We can't, we used it all.

MILDRED *looks over at* **ETHEL**. *Still ignoring everyone else, she's busy making magical incantations over her cauldron.*

I'll borrow some off Ethel.

MAUD *nods.* **MILDRED** *goes over to* **ETHEL**, *who is in an almost trance-like state, mumbling words under her breath and waving her arms about in a witchy manner.*

Ethel?

ETHEL What?

ETHEL *looks around – can't see the "invisible"* **MILDRED**. **MILDRED** *realises she can have fun, and taps* **ETHEL** *on her opposite shoulder.* **ETHEL** *whirls round.*

Who's there? This isn't funny!

MAUD *realises what's happening, and laughs.* MILDRED *taps* ETHEL *again.*

Stop it!

As ETHEL *looks for her unseen tormentor,* MILDRED *grabs some pondweed from* ETHEL's *cauldron. She takes the pondweed back to* MAUD *and throws it into their cauldron. They stir the potion as* MISS HARDBROOM *returns.*

MISS HARDBROOM The clock is ticking, girls.

DRUSILLA We're ready, Miss Hardbroom!

DRUSILLA *and* FENELLA *taste their potion and immediately collapse into gales of laughter.*

MISS HARDBROOM Adequately mirthful.

As DRUSILLA *goes to take another sip:*

That's enough – there is no need for hysteria. Let me test it.

MISS HARDBROOM *sips the potion.*

Ha. Ahahahaha. Ha. Not bad. B plus.

ETHEL I'm ready, Miss Hardbroom!

MISS HARDBROOM Gather round, everyone. I believe we are about to witness something rather special... *(looks at the* GIRLS *and frowns)* Where are Mildred and Maud?

DRUSILLA They sneaked out, Miss Hardbroom.

MILDRED No we—

MAUD *grabs* MILDRED.

MAUD *(sotto)* Shh, we'll just get into more trouble.

MISS HARDBROOM The school is protected by powerful spells. They won't have gone far. More's the pity. Now, we've wasted enough time. Ethel, your spell.

ETHEL *takes the stage, loving the attention.*

ETHEL She flutters lightly through the sky.

Behold – the human butterfly!

ETHEL *gracefully pirouettes over to her cauldron and takes an elegant sip of her potion. She moves her arms in a wing-like motion, expecting to take off...*

But instead, she clutches her stomach and falls to the ground, writhing and groaning. **DRUSILLA** *runs to her.*

DRUSILLA Ethel! You OK?

ETHEL *tries to reply to* **DRUSILLA,** *but when she opens her mouth, she can only snort.*

Ethel!

MISS HARDBROOM *(taking notes)* Interesting effect...

ETHEL *gets angry but can only make the snorting noise.* **MILDRED** *and* **MAUD** *can't help laughing.*

DRUSILLA What's happening to her?

MISS HARDBROOM *draws focus with her lecture as* **ETHEL** *"transforms" with* **ENID**'s *help.*

MISS HARDBROOM Let this be a lesson for all of you. When attempting a Transfiguration, the slightest mistake can have catastrophic results. For example, humans share fifty percent of their DNA with a simple banana.

DRUSILLA She's turning into a banana?

MISS HARDBROOM Not quite.

ETHEL *appears on all fours – transformed into a pig.*

ETHEL *snorts.*

DRUSILLA She's a pig!

MISS HARDBROOM *(examining* ETHEL*)* Barely. The spell was very poorly done. The morphic field is completely unstable—

DRUSILLA Can you change her back?

MISS HARDBROOM I'll do my best. But with this botched-up magic, it won't be easy. She could end up with a tail for weeks.

The ETHEL-*pig snorts in panic.*

Yes, Ethel, you may well snort with alarm. Perhaps next time, you will bother to measure your ingredients properly.

ETHEL *snorts indignantly and angrily – clearly trying to get a message across.*

DRUSILLA What's she saying?

MISS HARDBROOM Let us find out.

MISS HARDBROOM *makes a magical gesture and* ETHEL *is restored.*

DRUSILLA Ethy! You OK?

ETHEL *snorts.*

DRUSILLA Your tail's gone, anyway...

MISS HARDBROOM Ethel. I am *not* impressed.

ETHEL That was sabotage! Somebody tried to poison me!

MISS HARDBROOM Don't be so dramatic. You simply didn't add enough pondweed.

ETHEL I did! I measured out the exact amount! Someone must have tampered with my ingredients.

MISS HARDBROOM Remind me. What does *The Witches' Code* say about dealing with failure?

ETHEL "Don't fail". But Hallows don't fail! I'll do it again. I'll get it right this time... *(desperate)* Please let me do it again!

MILDRED *(suddenly)* It was my fault. I'm sorry.

MISS HARDBROOM Who said that?

No response.

Will the girl who said that please step forward?

MILDRED I'm here!

> **MISS HARDBROOM** *moves her hands, "divining"* **MILDRED**'s *position magically.*

MISS HARDBROOM *(sighs)* Mildred Hubble, I presume?

> **MISS HARDBROOM** *makes a magical gesture and snaps her fingers. The* **GIRLS** *jump as* **MILDRED** *is suddenly "visible" again.*

ETHEL *(furious) You* did – *that* to me!

MAUD It was my fault too.

> *Everyone looks around for* **MAUD**. **MISS HARDBROOM** *clicks her finger and* **MAUD** *becomes visible again.*

MISS HARDBROOM *(to* **MILDRED** *and* **MAUD***)* So, you were partners in crime.

MILDRED No. I took the pondweed, but I didn't know that would happen! I've never done magic before.

MISS HARDBROOM *Really?*

MILDRED I came here by accident. I'm supposed to be at another school and – I'm not even a witch at all.

Gasps from the **GIRLS** *(except* **MAUD***).*

ETHEL She's just an oik!

MISS HARDBROOM Language, Ethel.

ETHEL Sorry, I mean pleb.

MISS HARDBROOM Enough. Girls, you will tidy your things away while I speak with Miss Cackle. Class dismissed.

The **GIRLS** *tidy up.* **MILDRED** *approaches* **MISS HARDBROOM** *tentatively:*

MILDRED What about me? Shall I just go home? How do I get home?

MISS HARDBROOM Would it were that simple. You, Mildred Hubble, are a trespasser. Wait here while your fate is decided.

MISS HARDBROOM *leaves. Music. All the* **GIRLS** *go except* **MILDRED**, **MAUD** *and* **ETHEL**.

MILDRED What will they do to me?

MAUD They won't hurt you. I won't let them.

ETHEL You and whose coven? You can't help her. She's seen things only a witch should see.

MILDRED But – what if I became a witch? I could learn—

ETHEL Witches are born, not made. And you're about as magical as a cheese sandwich. Pleb.

MAUD Stop calling her that.

MILDRED I'd rather be a pleb than a snob.

ETHEL That's lucky then, Plebby McPleb, the plebbiest pleb in Plebtown. I wonder what they'll do to you. Maybe they'll just turn you into something that can't speak. Like a tree, or a rock. Or a worm. You look a bit like a worm. Your family won't even notice.

BAND *(sings)*
SHE BROKE THE CODE, SHE BROKE THE CODE,
NEVER MESS WITH THE WITCHES' CODE.
THEY'LL TURN YOU INTO A FROG OR A TOAD,
IF YOU MESS WITH THE CODE.
HEY, SHE'S MESSING WITH THE WITCHES' CODE.
SHE'S MESSING WITH THE WITCHES' CODE.

As the **BAND** *sing,* **MILDRED** *continues to stress, and* **MAUD** *consoles her. Simultaneously,* **MISS HARDBROOM** *visits* **MISS CACKLE** *in her study.*

MISS HARDBROOM It's regrettable, of course.

MISS CACKLE The poor child. I'm sure she meant no harm.

MISS HARDBROOM That is immaterial. The Code is very clear on the subject.

MISS CACKLE takes up the Code Book.

MISS CACKLE Is it? It's been ever so long since I read this thing...

MISS CACKLE searches through the book. Meanwhile, MILDRED seeks comfort from MAUD:

MILDRED I wouldn't really mind being a tree. I mean, I like camping.

ETHEL And you'd make a perfect toilet for the birds.

In MISS CACKLE's study, MISS CACKLE lays aside The Witches' Code with a sigh.

MISS CACKLE You're right, Hecate. Non-witches cannot be permitted to learn our secrets.

MISS HARDBROOM *(nods)* Will you deal with Mildred Hubble, or shall I?

MISS CACKLE I will do what must be done...but there's one thing I don't understand. How did she get past our protective spells?

MISS HARDBROOM *(frowns, slightly caught out)* I – transported her. She was with the other girls at the meeting place.

MISS CACKLE She shouldn't have been able to see them.

MISS HARDBROOM Perhaps the spells failed—

MISS CACKLE I cast them myself!

MISS CACKLE closes The Witches' Code book.

I think I need to speak to Mildred Hubble. Summon her, will you?

And, as quickly and magically as possible, **MISS HARDBROOM** *is gone and* **MILDRED** *is with* **MISS CACKLE.**

Well, Mildred. What am I to do with you?

MILDRED I'm sorry. Please, just let me go home.

MISS CACKLE I'm afraid I can't do that.

MILDRED I won't tell anyone, I promise. Please. My mum will be so worried—

MISS CACKLE Yes, I should talk to your mother.

MILDRED Don't hurt Mum! It wasn't her fault!

MISS CACKLE I'm not going to hurt anyone, child! I was simply going to remove all your memories of this place. That's the usual procedure.

MILDRED *(relieved)* Oh.

Then, slightly sad.

Oh... Could I maybe just remember Maud? And Tabby?

MISS CACKLE Why them?

MILDRED Maud's my friend. I've never really had a friend before. Or a cat.

MISS CACKLE And why is that?

MILDRED There's no pets in our building – oh, you mean the other thing? I guess I just – never really fit in.

MISS CACKLE Do you think you might fit in here?

MILDRED *(stunned)* Are you saying I can stay?

MISS CACKLE On a trial basis.

Offers a plate of buns.

Bun?

MILDRED Yes please!

MISS CACKLE To the school or the bun?

MILDRED Both! But...why?

MISS CACKLE There's something special about you, Mildred Hubble. I would like to find out what it is. Only a witch should be able to see through our protective spells.

MILDRED So could I really be magical? Even if my family aren't?

MISS CACKLE It's never happened before. But *you* are not your family. Not one of us is. Thank the Grand High Witch.

MILDRED What do you mean?

MISS CACKLE Every family has its demons and, sadly, I mean that literally. Inherited curses are two-a-penny in magical families, but we Cackles suffer from a particularly embarrassing condition.

> **MISS CACKLE** *beckons* **MILDRED** *closer.* **MILDRED** *leans in.*

Evil Twin Syndrome.

MILDRED Evil Twin Syndrome?

MISS CACKLE In your world, it's mostly confined to certain soap operas. But for witches, it's a clear and present danger. Look at this picture.

> **MISS CACKLE** *shows* **MILDRED** *a picture.*

What do you see?

MILDRED It's you – but wearing a wig.

MISS CACKLE If only. That is my sister, Agatha Cackle.

MILDRED Oh. Right.

MISS CACKLE Alas, due to the family curse, all the evil from both our souls ran into Agatha. She was born with a raging desire to possess all that I have, and destroy it.

MILDRED Including the school?

MISS CACKLE Especially this school. Since I inherited the family business, she has tried to take over many times and always failed – but I fear we have not seen the back of her.

MILDRED Why are you telling me all this?

MISS CACKLE To make you see that no family is perfect, and you should never be ashamed of where you come from. Also, you never know, it may turn out to be important later. Now, would you like to speak to your mother and ask for permission to stay?

MILDRED Yes!

MUSIC: "WITCHING KIND" - (BAND) REPRISE.

Int. Miss Cackle's Academy – Potions Lab

MILDRED *runs in to join* MAUD.

MILDRED I can stay! I can stay!

MILDRED *and* MAUD *hug and jump around.*

MAUD We're going to be witches together!

MILDRED Yes!

Then, anxious:

But what if Ethel's right? And I'm as magical as a cheese sandwich?

MAUD Don't say that. You can do this. I'll help you.

MILDRED Really?

MAUD Cheese sandwiches are my favourite.

Montage 1 of Academy Scenes

Music. The GIRLS *move between scenes quickly, creating little vignettes.*

MISS DRILL *jogs on, a sports whistle around her neck.*

MISS DRILL First things first. Hovering. Sticks on the ground.

The GIRLS *place their broomsticks on the ground.*

Now, say it loud, say it proud – *Hover!*

With the help of ENID, *the sticks hover on command.*

ETHEL Hover!

DRUSILLA Hover!

FENELLA Hover!

MAUD Hover!

MILDRED Hover!

MISS DRILL Come on, Hubble! Give it some welly. Show that broom who's boss!

MILDRED *holds her hand to her broomstick, commanding it:*

MILDRED Hover. Hover!

It works! MILDRED *and* MAUD *celebrate.*

Music. MILDRED *in front of* MISS HARDBROOM, *answering a question...*

For a Kingmaker spell, the ratio should be three parts eye of newt to one part toe of frog.

MISS HARDBROOM That is... correct.

ETHEL *frowns.* MAUD *grins. Music.*

Back to the broomstick. **MILDRED***'s trying to persuade*
TABBY *to climb on:*

MILDRED Go on, Tabs. It's not that scary – really.

> **TABBY** *mews in terror.* **MISS HARDBROOM** *watches,*
> *disapproving.*

MISS HARDBROOM If that animal cannot learn to fly, he will
have to be replaced.

> **TABBY** *mews and clings to* **MILDRED.**

MILDRED No, please! I love Tabby! You can't split us up! Please?

MISS HARDBROOM Mildred Hubble. A witch does not whine
when things don't go her way. A witch *makes* things go her
way. Do I make myself clear?

MILDRED Yes, Miss Hardbroom.

> *Music. Potions class.*

MAUD Laughter potion take two – here we go!

> **MILDRED** *and* **MAUD** *"cheers" with tiny phials and drink*
> *the potion – then burst into hysterical laughter!*

DRUSILLA Wow! Mildred's got so much better in three weeks!

ETHEL Only because of that miserable Maud...

> **ENID** *bounds onto the stage carrying piles of luggage,*
> *a cat basket and her broom.*

ENID *Finally*! I'm here, witches!

Miss Cackle's Study

ENID *joins* MISS HARDBROOM *and* MISS CACKLE.

MISS CACKLE Miss Hardbroom, this is our new girl, Enid Nightshade.

ENID How's it hanging, Miss C?

MISS CACKLE Excellently, thank you, Enid.

ENID HB?

MISS HARDBROOM *(raises an eyebrow) Nightshade?* I thought your family always went to Pentangles Academy.

MISS CACKLE Until now.

To ENID.

Run along dear, you've got Chanting class next.

ENID Laters, witches.

ENID *goes.* MISS HARDBROOM *looks very disapproving.*

MISS CACKLE This is a great honour for us, Hecate. I *do* hope she will be happy here.

MISS HARDBROOM Nightshade or not, I shall treat the girl the same as any other witch.

MISS CACKLE Yes, that's what I'm afraid of.

Chanting Room

The GIRLS *are impressed with* ENID. FENELLA *and* DRUSILLA *take selfies with her.* ETHEL *smarms up to* ENID.

ETHEL Well met. I am Ethel Hallow.

Waits for a reaction that doesn't come.

Hallow. You know. *Hallow.* One of the most famous witching families.

MAUD *(to* MILDRED*)* Not as famous as the Nightshades. Or as rich.

ETHEL *(to* ENID*)* It's an honour to meet you.

ENID *(sounding uninterested)* OK. Hi, Elsie.

MISS BAT *enters. A seemingly doddery old lady, she conceals a sharp witching mind.*

MISS BAT Well met, girls.

GIRLS Well met, Miss Bat.

MISS BAT I hope you're all in fine voice today, girls. Let's start with "Mother Moon".

MISS BAT *takes her place at the keyboard. The* GIRLS *sing.* ENID *is deliberately out of tune.*

GIRLS *(sing)*
MOTHER MOON, WE RISE TO GREET YOU
HUMBLY AT THIS MIDNIGHT HOUR
WHEN THE WORLD IS CLOAKED IN DARKNESS
YOU ARE LIGHT AND YOU ARE POWER...

MISS BAT *stops playing.*

MISS BAT No, no, no, girls! You're all over the place!

ETHEL Perhaps I should sing a solo – to show the others how it's done.

MISS BAT Chanting isn't about showing off.

It's about witches magnifying their powers by working together in perfect harmony. Try again, and this time *listen* to each other.

GIRLS *(sing)*
WAXING, WANING, GROWING, FADING,
FAST ROTATING, SLOWLY SPINNING,
CIRCLES WITHIN CIRCLES
NEVER ENDING OR BEGINNING.

> **MILDRED** *glances at* **ENID** – *she's now singing even more obviously, and loudly, out of tune.* **MILDRED** *suppresses a giggle.*

MISS BAT Sing up, girls! Sing up!

GIRLS
HOLD THE CIRCLE, HOLD THE CIRCLE,
HOLD THE CIRCLE EVERMORE.

> **ENID** *glances at* **MILDRED** – *mischievous. And increases her efforts. She's now bellowing, way off the note. The other* **GIRLS** *are glancing at her.* **MILDRED** *can barely contain herself.*

HOLD THE CIRCLE, HOLD THE CIRCLE,

> **MISS BAT** *stops playing and stares at* **ENID**. *The other* **GIRLS** *stop singing but* **ENID** *continues:*

ENID *(in an impossibly deep, man's bass voice)*
HOLD THE CIRCLE EVERMORE.

> *Everyone stares at* **ENID**. **MISS BAT** *looks around, bewildered, for the source of the extraordinary voice.*

MISS BAT Enid – was that *you?*

> **ENID**, *fake-innocent, looks around and behind her, "puzzled", and shrugs.*

MILDRED *explodes in uncontrollable laughter.* ENID *looks at her with an expression of bewildered innocence – which just makes* MILDRED *laugh all the more. She laughs and laughs, until she suddenly realises that all the other* GIRLS *are staring in the same direction –* MISS HARDBROOM's *appeared again.* MILDRED *abruptly stops laughing.*

MISS HARDBROOM Mildred Hubble! I might have known. Whenever there is chaos and disruption, it always comes down to you! Will you ever learn to take witching seriously?

ENID *takes this information on board.*

ENID It was me, Miss Hardbroom. I told her a joke.

MISS HARDBROOM A *joke*? In *Chanting class*?

ENID It was the one about the warlock and the tiny broomstick, do you know it?

MISS HARDBROOM I do not, nor do I wish to. Enid, I know this is your first day, so I will make allowances.

ETHEL *puts her hand up.*

Yes, Ethel.

ETHEL Enid needs somebody to take her in hand. To show her around, and help her settle in—

ENID Awesome. I choose Mildred!

MILDRED *Me?!*

MISS HARDBROOM No. Mildred is – not at all suitable.

ENID I don't understand. Miss Cackle told Mummy that every single girl here is a hard-working, talented witch.

MISS HARDBROOM *(containing her annoyance)* She said that, did she?

(resigned) Very well. Mildred, Enid is now your responsibility.

The school bell rings.

ENID Wicked. Come on, Mils!

ENID *drags* **MILDRED** *out after her.* **MAUD** *watches, a bit left out...*

ETHEL *(to* **MAUD,** *sotto)* That didn't take long.

MAUD What?

ETHEL She's already dumped you for someone better. Plebs are notorious social climbers.

MAUD Oh, bore off, you slimy slug.

ETHEL Just watch her. You'll see...

Montage 2 of Academy Scenes

Music. Time passes during a quick montage of scenes, mirroring the previous one:

Potions Lab: the GIRLS *are two to a cauldron.* ENID *now with* MILDRED, MAUD *on her own.* MILDRED *and* ENID'*s potion explodes.*

MISS HARDBROOM And *that* is why there is no room for sloppiness in witchcraft. Start again from scratch.

MILDRED looks embarrassed but ENID *laughs it off. Soon* MILDRED *is laughing too.* MAUD *looks on...*

Classroom. MILDRED *stands in front of* MISS HARDBROOM.

MILDRED *Cold* spell? I thought you said an *old* spell.

MISS HARDBROOM Mildred Hubble. Have you done the wrong revision *again*?

MAUD *sighs and writes something on her book.*

MILDRED I, um...

MAUD *shows her what she's written.*

(grateful) Cold spell. Reindeer blood and penguin's heart...

MISS HARDBROOM *(not looking at* MILDRED*)* Correct so far...

ENID *nudges* MILDRED *and shows her something she's written down.*

MILDRED Polar bear poo and snowman's fart—

MILDRED *looks at* ENID *- that can't be right!* MAUD *groans and buries her face in her hands.* ENID *laughs.*

MISS HARDBROOM I suppose that sort of crudity passes for humour where you come from. Perhaps it's a good thing that you will soon be back there.

MAUD *looks really concerned…*

Broomstick Field: **MILDRED** *is trying to encourage* **TABBY** *to ride the broomstick.*

MILDRED Tabby still won't get on the broom.

ENID Forget about it! Let's have a race! To the Spooky Forest and back.

MILDRED But we're not supposed to—

ENID You're *supposed* to be looking after me, remember? Well I'm going anyway.

MAUD Millie, you can't! HB warned you. If you carry on like this you're going to get expelled!

ENID So? I've been expelled seventeen times. If you don't count nursery.

MILDRED You got expelled from *nursery*?

ENID Not exactly. My first nursery burned down, that's all. Well, I burned it down. But it was an accident. Sort of.

To **MILDRED.**

You coming or what?

ENID *takes off.*

MILDRED *(to* **MAUD***)* Sorry, I promised to look after her—

MILDRED *follows* **ENID.** **MAUD** *yells after her:*

MAUD Millie, be careful!

Yells and thumps offstage – a big crash…

*...*MILDRED *returns, crestfallen, holding her broomstick, which is broken in half. Followed by* ENID, *who thinks it's all hilarious.*

MISS DRILL I'll put it down in the accident book – well, books, you've filled up quite a few—

MILDRED I know.

MAUD Millie, are you OK?

MILDRED I'm fine...

MAUD Well your broomstick isn't! And it's Hallowe'en tonight!

ENID Who cares about stupid Hallowe'en?

> MISS HARDBROOM *enters.* ETHEL, DRUSILLA *and* FENELLA *gather around.*

MISS HARDBROOM Hallowe'en is one of the most solemn and significant nights in the witching calendar. You girls will be performing a broomstick formation in front of the world's most distinguished witches.

Therefore, there will be no tomfoolery, no hijinks, buffoonery, capers or japery –

Glancing at MILDRED.

and most particularly, no shenanigans. What will there not be?

GIRLS Tomfoolery, hijinks, buffoonery, capers, japery, shenanigans.

> ETHEL'*s hand shoots up.*

MISS HARDBROOM Yes, Ethel?

ETHEL Who will lead the flight, Miss Hardbroom?

MISS HARDBROOM An excellent question, Ethel. At Miss Cackle's request, that honour will go to Maud Spellbody.

MAUD *(shocked) Me?*

ETHEL *(outraged) Her?*

MILDRED Well done, Maud, that's brilliant!

MAUD *glances at* MILDRED – *still a bit hurt about* ENID.

MISS HARDBROOM Yes, Maud. So far this term, you have shown the most improvement in flying.

ETHEL But that's not fair! How could I improve? I was perfect to start with!

MISS HARDBROOM Ethel, remind us all what *The Witches' Code* says about fairness.

ETHEL *(sullen)* Life isn't fair. Get over it.

MISS HARDBROOM Then I suggest you do so. Now, girls, make sure your broomsticks are clean, polished – *(she notices* MILDRED*'s broken broomstick)* and *whole.*

MISS HARDBROOM *leaves.* MILDRED *picks up her broken broomstick:*

MILDRED *(to* MAUD, *gutted)* How could I be so stupid? She's going to expel me for sure!

ENID Here, take my broomstick. I don't mind one more expulsion.

MAUD No, take mine!

ENID Mine's a genuine antique Nightrider. It cost Dad a fortune.

MAUD *(to* MILDRED*)* But *I'm* your best friend!

MILDRED *looks between her two friends, torn. Doesn't want to have to choose:*

MILDRED It's OK. I can fix this.

MILDRED *heads off with her broken broomstick.* MAUD*'s a bit hurt.* ENID *realises and feels bad for* MAUD. ETHEL *has a brilliant idea, and follows* MILDRED. DRUSILLA *automatically follows* ETHEL.

ETHEL *(to* DRUSILLA*)* Wait there.

DRUSILLA Why?

ETHEL You'll see.

Obediently, DRUSILLA *stays.* ENID *goes over to* MAUD*.*

ENID You know what? Why don't you borrow my broomstick tonight?

MAUD *(sarky)* What, your "genuine antique Nightrider"?

Suspicious.

Why?

ENID You're the best flyer – you should have the best broom.

Tempting.

Go on, just take it...

MAUD *(snaps)* Stop trying to buy us with broomsticks! I'm not for sale and nor is Millie.

ENID All right, don't be like that—

"MILDRED" *(really* ETHEL *in magical disguise!) enters.*

MAUD Mildred, tell your *friend* that I don't need charity.

"MILDRED" Oh, not this again!

MAUD What do you mean?

"MILDRED" I'm just so bored of your jealousy. In fact, I'm bored of you.

MAUD *(shocked and upset)* Mildred!

"MILDRED" *(to* MAUD*)* I've tried to be friends with you and Enid, but you won't let me. Fine. I choose Enid! Now will you leave me alone?

Devastated, MAUD *struggles not to cry.*

MAUD OK.

MAUD *walks off.*

ENID Mildred!

"MILDRED" What? It had to be said.

ENID No it didn't! You go and tell her right now that you didn't mean it.

"MILDRED" Why are you taking her side?

ENID 'Cos I wanted to be friends with the class clown, not the school bully.

"MILDRED" *(angry) I am not a bully!*

Then, calming down.

You've got it all wrong... I just lost it, that's all. I'm really sorry—

ENID Don't tell me, tell Maud.

"MILDRED" I will... I'll just take this for her...

"MILDRED" *picks up* MAUD'*s broomstick. She quietly mutters some words into it and makes magical gestures.*

DRUSILLA What are you doing?

"MILDRED" A Good Luck Charm for tonight. So she knows I'm on her side.

DRUSILLA, FENELLA *and* ENID *watch* "MILDRED" *walk off with the broomstick.*

School Grounds

Hallowe'en music. A huge full moon. Cold, wintry lighting. As the GIRLS *sing the moon chant, the feeling should be solemn, eldritch, eerie. Candle or lantern light if possible.*

GIRLS *(sing)*
MOTHER MOON, WE RISE TO GREET YOU
HUMBLY AT THIS TWILIGHT HOUR
WHEN THE WORLD IS CLOAKED IN DARKNESS
YOU ARE THE LIGHT, YOU ARE THE POWER...
WAXING, WANING, GROWING, FADING,
FAST ROTATING, SLOWLY SPINNING.
HOLD THE CIRCLE, HOLD THE CIRCLE,
HOLD THE CIRCLE EVERMORE.
HOLD THE CIRCLE, HOLD THE CIRCLE,
HOLD THE CIRCLE EVERMORE.

MISS HARDBROOM prepares for the broomstick display.
MISS CACKLE goes into the audience to welcome them.

MISS CACKLE Well met all, and a very special welcome to our guests of honour.

MISS CACKLE produces some ornate, flowing robes.

The Supreme Sorceress herself!

MISS CACKLE places the robes on an audience member.

And the Grand High Witch!

Again, she gives the robes to an audience member. Then returns to the stage.

To open the festivities, I am delighted to introduce a broomstick display from our First Form – the witches of the future!

MISS HARDBROOM Ready, girls... And, begin.

The GIRLS *rise into the air on their broomsticks. NB:* MILDRED's *broomstick is poorly mended with duct tape.*

The brooms rise and fall gracefully. A smattering of applause...

And suddenly, MAUD *is struggling to control her broomstick. It kicks like a bucking bronco.* MAUD's *broomstick turns completely around and heads in the wrong direction.*

MISS CACKLE Well, this certainly makes a change from the usual style...

DRUSILLA Maud! What are you doing?

MAUD It's my broomstick! It's gone crazy! Help!

MILDRED I'll save you!

MAUD No! Please don't!

MILDRED *flies over to* MAUD *and grabs her, but it doesn't stop* MAUD's *broom from veering wildly about.*

Millie, let go! You're making it worse!

MILDRED Sorry!

MAUD The broomstick can't hold both of us! We'll crash.

MILDRED *and* MAUD *struggle to stay on the same broomstick.*

Get on your own stick! No – Millie, not the moon! NOT MY MOON!

MILDRED *grabs onto the full moon itself, breaking it.*

MISS HARDBROOM Mildred Hubble!

MISS CACKLE *(to the audience)* I'm so sorry, everyone.

All the GIRLS *are mortified except* ENID.

MISS HARDBROOM If these are the witches of the future, I shudder to think what the future will be like.

ENID Fun?

MISS HARDBROOM gives ENID a freezing glance.

MISS CACKLE My dear guests, I do apologise. But we won't let this ruin our night! We'll light the magical fires and start the chanting... Miss Hardbroom, deal with your First Form.

MISS HARDBROOM I certainly shall.

MISS CACKLE takes the robes and ushers the "guests" back to the audience, leaving the GIRLS of the first year alone with MISS HARDBROOM.

Well? What have you to say for yourselves?

MAUD I don't know what happened! My broomstick just went out of control!

MISS HARDBROOM examines MAUD's broomstick.

MISS HARDBROOM And no wonder. This broomstick has been cursed – with a Shenanigans Spell.

ENID *(laughs)* Nice one!

MISS HARDBROOM Who is responsible for this?

No response. The GIRLS' eyes slide around to MILDRED.

Unless the guilty party owns up, you will *all* be severely punished—

DRUSILLA It was Mildred!

MILDRED No!

DRUSILLA We all saw you cast a spell on Maud's broomstick!

MILDRED I didn't! I'd never do that to Maud!

DRUSILLA Liar! You said it was a Good Luck Charm – didn't she, Enid?

MISS HARDBROOM Enid?

ENID *(looks down)* I'm not a snitch. Whoever did it, it was probably just a prank – *(looks at* **MILDRED***)* right?

MILDRED Maud, I promise, I never touched your broomstick.

FENELLA / DRUSILLA She's lying! / You did / We saw you *(etc.)*

MILDRED I'd never hurt you, Maud! You're my best friend.

MAUD *(sad, quiet)* That's not what you said before.

MILDRED *What?*

MISS HARDBROOM Mildred Hubble, several witnesses saw you tampering with Maud's broomstick. Tomorrow, I will decide what your punishment will be.

MILDRED But I—

MISS HARDBROOM Now go to your rooms. All of you!

The **GIRLS** *disperse, muttering angrily about how it isn't fair. Only* **ETHEL** *has a smile on her face.*

MILDRED Maud!

But **MAUD** *walks on.*

Enid! You believe me, don't you?

ENID Mildred. I *saw* you.

MILDRED*'s too stunned to respond.* **ENID** *walks on.* **MILDRED** *runs after her.* **ETHEL***'s loving this.*

DRUSILLA *(to* **ETHEL***)* Worst Hallowe'en ever.

ETHEL *can't help boasting.*

ETHEL Not for me. I think I've finally managed to get rid of Mildred Hubble.

DRUSILLA *You've* got rid of her? *I* saw her put the spell on Maud's broomstick. You weren't even there!

ETHEL Wasn't I?

DRUSILLA *(confused)* I don't know, were you there or not?

ETHEL Put it like this. *Somebody* might have used a Looky-Likey Spell to disguise herself as Mildred, picked a fight with Maud and cursed her broomstick. But nobody will ever be able to prove it.

> **DRUSILLA** *stares at* **ETHEL** – *stunned...*

BAND

> SHE BROKE THE CODE, SHE BROKE THE CODE,
> NEVER MESS WITH THE WITCHES' CODE
> THEY'LL TURN YOU INTO A FROG OR A TOAD
> IF YOU MESS WITH THE CODE.

Mildred's Room

A miserable **MILDRED** *confides in* **TABBY***:*

MILDRED You heard them, Tabs. They all lied about me. Even Enid. And Maud believes them...

TABBY *mews sympathetically.*

HB will expel me tomorrow for sure. Not that I even want to stay, now.

TABBY *purrs and cuddles* **MILDRED***.*

Oh, Tabby. It's OK. I'll take you with me. If they'll let me...

TABBY *mews urgently.*

You're right. They won't let me. They won't even let me remember this place.

TABBY *goes over to* **MILDRED***'s broomstick, paws at it and mews.*

That's right, Tabby. We need to run away – right now! That's right, Tabby – in the bag! Come on!

MILDRED *puts* **TABBY** *in her schoolbag, picks up her broom and sneaks out. She runs with her broomstick until she crashes into an invisible barrier.*

What was that?

She tries again. Crashes again.

Of course! The protective spells.

MILDRED *puts* **TABBY** *down in his satchel.*

Good boy, Tabby...

MILDRED *tries again and again to break through the invisible barrier. She fails.*

(crumbling) That's it. We can't get out. I'm going to lose everything. And I won't even know what I've lost...

MISS HARDBROOM *appears in* **MILDRED**'s *mind.*

MISS HARDBROOM A witch does not whine when things don't go her way. A witch *makes* things go her way.

MILDRED Shut up, Miss Hardbroom! You've won! I'm leaving!

Then, with new energy.

But I'm going to do it *my* way.

Sings.

ALL THE TIMES I TRIED TO DO
WHATEVER I WAS TOLD TO DO
NEVER BEING GOOD ENOUGH
HOWEVER HARD I TRIED.
I'M SICK OF COMING LAST.

IT'S TIME TO GET OUT FAST.
BEFORE THEY STOP ME.
BEFORE THEY STOP ME.

ALL THE TIMES MISS HARDBROOM RANTED
ALL THE SCHEMES THAT ETHEL PLANTED
EVERYTHING I TOOK FOR GRANTED
DOESN'T MATTER NOW...

I'M DISENCHANTED.

DISENCHANTED WITH THIS SCHOOL.
NO LONGER WILL THEY MOCK ME, WON'T BE THEIR FOOL.
I'M GONNA GET OUT BEFORE THEY STOP ME, BEFORE THEY
    STOP ME.

I'M SICK OF COMING LAST.
IT'S TIME TO GET OUT FAST.
BEFORE THEY STOP ME.
BEFORE THEY STOP ME.

I'M SICK OF COMING LAST.
IT'S TIME TO GET OUT FAST.

BEFORE THEY STOP ME.
BEFORE THEY STOP ME.

THESE BOOTS WERE MADE FOR WITCHING
BUT THAT'S NOT WHAT THEY'LL DO
TRY AND CAGE ME IN AND THEY WILL STOMP ALL OVER YOU.

I'M SICK OF COMING LAST.
IT'S TIME TO GET OUT FAST.
BEFORE THEY STOP ME...
BEFORE THEY STOP ME...

MILDRED *approaches the invisible barrier. Determined.
Driven by the emotional power of her song. She picks
up her broomstick (already taped together) and snaps
it in half. She holds the two halves triumphantly aloft.*

(spoken) LET ME GO!

*An ominous sound of thunder as the magical barrier
is removed.* **MILDRED** *clutches her ears...*

OK... So that was a bit dramatic...

MILDRED *approaches the barrier.*

I did it! I can get through!

Waving her arm about to test the barrier.

I made a gap... Quite a big gap actually...

Suddenly runs round in panic.

Oh no... Please tell me I didn't bring the whole thing down...?

MILDRED *runs around frantically testing the barrier –
it's quite clear that that's exactly what she's done.*

Oh Tabs, we're in trouble now...

Remembers.

But who cares? We're not even at this school any more!
Come on Tabs, we're leaving!

With her head held high, **MILDRED** *walks through the barrier, carrying* **TABBY** *in his bag. Music.*

The Mountainside

MILDRED *descends down the perilous mountainside.*
She's clutching TABBY, *who mews plaintively.*

MILDRED It's OK, Tabs. Nothing to be scared of. Only the dark.
There's nothing here but us, and trees, and...

An owl hoots. TABBY *yelps.*

...an owl...

A wolf howls.

And that's just a...wolf...

TABBY *mews and clutches at* MILDRED.

No, we can't go back now. We've come too far. Just be brave...
Look, there's a light. Somebody's there. Maybe they can
help us...

The trees part to reveal AGATHA.

AGATHA Oh, Sister. How long I've been waiting for this moment.
And how delicious that it should happen on Hallowe'en.

MILDRED *peeps through trees and watches.*

MILDRED *(sotto)* It's Miss Cackle!

TABBY *shakes his head and mews – "no".*

(sotto) You're right! That's not Miss Cackle – it must be her
evil twin! Lucky she warned us about her.

AGATHA *(menacing, unaware of* MILDRED*)* No, my goody-goody-
good-for-nothing sister. I don't know why your protective
spells failed –

MILDRED *gasps, guilty.*

– but finally, I have the chance to take control of *my* school! And you, your pathetic teachers and your miserable pupils will bow to my will – or be destroyed!

AGATHA *lets out a full-on evil cackle. The trees join in.*

And *that* is how a Cackle should cackle! *Sister*!

AGATHA *sweeps offstage.* MILDRED *turns to* TABBY.

MILDRED I know I said I'd never go back – but I have to warn them! I can't let Agatha hurt them.

TABBY *(mews)*

MILDRED No, not even Ethel.

Determined.

Come on, Tabby. We're going back to the school!

Dramatic music.

Epilogue

MISS CACKLE *comes on from the wings, leading the applause.* **ETHEL** *follows her.*

MISS CACKLE Well done, girls!

To the audience.

Aren't they doing well?

MAUD *pushes the mirror on.*

MAUD All to stage for interval reset please! Please prepare for Act Two costume and make-up changes –

Seeing **MISS CACKLE.**

Miss Cackle, you were totally amazing as Agatha, we were well impressed – let us know if you need anyone to help you with your make-up?

ETHEL Miss Cackle, may I have a word?

MISS CACKLE Certainly, Ethel. Is there a problem?

ETHEL Yes! I hate Mildred's stupid play. She's made me look like some sort of...bully.

MISS CACKLE To be fair, dear, you did do every one of those things.

ETHEL Ages ago! We were first years!

MISS CACKLE True, but it's only fair to point out that there were similar incidents in the second, third and fourth years.

ETHEL Well, the fifth year will be *very* different.

MISS CACKLE That's the spirit! Break a leg in the second half, dear.

MISS CACKLE *heads off.* **ETHEL** *stares mutinously after her.*

ETHEL Oh, I do hope so.

To the audience.

What are you looking at, plebs? Go and stuff yourselves with ice cream.

ETHEL *pushes the mirror after* **MISS CACKLE.** **MAUD** *appears with her cans.*

MAUD Mavis! Iron coming in.

The iron comes down. As it does so...

Interval set and costume change – go! Go house lights, go ice cream sellers, go...everyone.

End of Act One

ACT TWO

Prologue

MAUD *is onstage, with her cans:*

MAUD Act Two Beginners please. ACT TWO BEGINNERS PLEASE!

Bumps into ENID.

Enid, that means we're about to start the second half—

ENID I know what it means, you sneaky witch!

MAUD *(indignant)* What d'you mean, sneaky?

ENID So, when *I* want to put a spell on Ethel, you're all like no, it's totally against the rules. And what do I find in the dressing room?

ENID *shows* MAUD *a small leaf.*

MAUD That's dragonsbane! The active ingredient in a—

ENID / MAUD Svengali Obedience Spell.

MAUD But it's restricted. Even the fifth years can't use it unsupervised!

ENID *I know.*

MAUD Where did you find it?

ENID I told you, in the dressing room. Something you're not telling me?

MAUD *I* didn't put a spell on her!

ENID Then why hasn't she tried to ruin the show yet?

MAUD   I don't know... *(thinks)* Maybe *she* brought the dragonsbane?

ENID She's planning something, isn't she?

MAUD Keep an eye on her. And keep her away from Mildred!

ENID *darts off backstage as Act Two proper starts...*

Clearance. Ready, Mavis? Miss Bat? Miss Drill? Miss Cackle, are you happy? OK – go Act Two!

The **BAND** *strike up the music for Act Two.*

The Mountainside

AGATHA *(sings)*
EVERY TRUE WITCH RECOGNISES
BEING NICE DON'T WIN NO PRIZES.
AND THE SISTER I DESPISE IS GONNA FALL.
YOU WOULD NOT TAKE MY ADVICE, SIS.
SO IT'S NO MORE MRS NICE WITCH.
NOW I'M GONNA SHOW MY POWER.
WELCOME TO THE WITCHING HOUR.

A BIG OLD CHANGE IS COMING DOWN
I'LL PUT AN END TO DUMBING DOWN
NOBODY GONNA RUN ME DOWN NO MORE.
I'M NOT A GIVER, NOT A SHARER.
I PREFER TO RULE BY TERROR.
YES WE'RE GONNA SHOW OUR POWER,
WELCOME TO THE WITCHING HOUR.

FLAME, SMOKE, BRIMSTONE,
DIRT, ASH, DUST, BONE,
FIRE, LET THE HEAVENS RAIN.
OCEANS FREEZING MOUNTAINS FALLING
LIGHTNING FLASHING THUNDER ROLLING
SEAS ARE BURNING WORLD STOPS TURNING –
AND I'M BORN AGAIN

BY THE WINGS OF RAVENS BEATING,
NO MORE KIDDIES TRICK OR TREATING.
THE WHOLE WORLD WILL BE GREETING MY NEW DAWN.
BY THE MIGHT OF STORMS AND BLIZZARDS,
NO MORE LOVABLE BOY WIZARDS.
TIME FOR US TO SHOW OUR POWER.
PLEBS WILL FLEE AND BEG AND COWER.
WELCOME TO, WELCOME TO THE WITCHING HOUR.

(speaks) Sister, we shall meet at midnight. In *my* school.

AGATHA *gets on her broomstick and flies off dramatically.*

Mildred's Room

Back at the school, it's the middle of the night and very, very dark. MAUD *sneaks into* MILDRED*'s room.*

MAUD Mildred? Mildred!

Suddenly she crashes into DRUSILLA*:*

MAUD / DRUSILLA Aargh!

Then, to each other:

Shh!

MAUD Drusilla! What are you doing here?

DRUSILLA I wanted to talk to Mildred – why are *you* here?

MAUD Same. Where is she?

DRUSILLA She's gone. And she's taken Tabby. I think she's run away.

MAUD Oh, no... It's my fault.

DRUSILLA No it isn't.

MAUD I should have stood up for her. Even though she was so horrible to me.

DRUSILLA No she wasn't. *(off* MAUD*'s surprise)* That was Ethel. She disguised herself as Mildred. With a Looky-Likey Spell.

MAUD And you *knew* about this?

DRUSILLA Not at first... I couldn't sleep. I had to tell Mildred...

MAUD She can't have got far. Come on, let's go find her.

DRUSILLA We can't. We'll be in so much trouble—

MAUD I don't care.

MAUD *heads off.*

Dark Corridor – Night

MAUD creeps along the corridor. Unseen by MAUD, *two bright eyes are watching her. It's* ETHEL's *cat, Nightstar, following* MAUD.

Dark Corridor / Ethel's Room – Night

ETHEL *is in magical communication with Nightstar.*

ETHEL Nightstar? ...What is it? Maud Spellbody is doing *what*? Show me, my familiar. Let me see through your eyes...

MAUD *creeps along the corridor...and bumps into* MILDRED.

MAUD / MILDRED Aargh!

MAUD Mildred?

MILDRED *(simultaneously)* Maud?

ETHEL *(seeing through Nightstar's eyes)* Mildred.

MILDRED / MAUD *(simultaneously)* I'm sorry...

MAUD Me first. I should have stood up for you. But Ethel tricked me—

MILDRED That's OK. We've got much bigger problems now.

MAUD What?

MILDRED Is there anywhere we can hide?

MAUD Broom cupboard!

MAUD *opens a broom cupboard and she and* MILDRED *climb inside.* TABBY *stays outside the cupboard. Nightstar is still watching...*

ETHEL Well done, Nightstar. Now we've got them.

ETHEL *creeps out of her room...*

Dark Corridor / Broom Cupboard

A sotto but urgent conversation between **MILDRED** *and*
MAUD *as they hide in the broom cupboard:*

MILDRED I climbed down the mountain, and I saw Agatha!

MAUD Miss Cackle's evil twin sister!

MILDRED She's trying to take over the school – tonight.

MAUD It's OK, she can't get past the protective spells... Wait a
minute, how did *you* get *out*?

MILDRED Um...

MAUD You took down the protective spells?!

MILDRED I'm sorry! I didn't mean to!

ETHEL *creeps along the corridor towards the broom
cupboard...*

MAUD Where is she now?

MILDRED I don't know. She might already be here.

ETHEL *shuts the cupboard door and locks it.*

MAUD We have to warn Miss Cackle!

MAUD *tries to open the cupboard door but can't.*

The door's stuck.

MILDRED Let me try!

MILDRED *and* **MAUD** *rattle the door – at first trying to
be quiet, then with increasing desperation.*

MAUD We're trapped!

MILDRED Help!

MAUD Don't! Agatha might hear us!

MILDRED OK. It's just a door. There must be a spell we can use...

MAUD I can't remember any.

MILDRED Wait, I know one... Open Sesame!

Nothing happens.

I really thought that would work.

MAUD It does, but you have to get the gestures right. And we don't do those till next year.

TABBY *trots away.*

Meanwhile, **ETHEL** *heads to* **MISS CACKLE***'s study:*

Corridor by Miss Cackle's Study

ETHEL *knocks on the door.*

ETHEL Miss Cackle! Miss Cackle?

*No reply. But "*MISS CACKLE*" appears in the shadows behind her...*

AGATHA *(as* MISS CACKLE*)* Hello, dear. Is there a problem?

ETHEL Miss Cackle! I heard a noise and I thought it was burglars! So I locked them in the broom cupboard.

AGATHA Well done, dear. But you needn't have worried. All the girls' rooms are protected by magic.

ETHEL But it wasn't burglars. It was Mildred and Maud. Breaking rules and sneaking around at night.

AGATHA Naughty, naughty girls. Young witches should stay in their beds at night – you never know what evil monsters may be on the prowl...

AGATHA *suddenly looks terrifying – and the penny drops for* ETHEL.

ETHEL Y– you're not Miss Cackle, are you?

AGATHA Oh, I am Miss Cackle. But probably not the one you were expecting.

ETHEL If you're Agatha, that's OK... I've always liked evil twins... My name's Ethel Hallow, maybe we can work together?

AGATHA I don't do double acts. Not any more.

AGATHA *makes a magical gesture, and turns* ETHEL *into a snail.*

I've always had a soft spot for snails. So much nicer than children.

AGATHA *knocks on the door of* MISS CACKLE*'s office.*

Oh, Sister dear? I know you can hear me. I've already turned one of your brats into a snail. And I know where to find two more. So if you care about your girls at all, let me in and face me like a witch!

The door to MISS CACKLE's *office slowly opens and* AGATHA *goes in, followed slowly by the* ETHEL-*snail.*

Corridor by Broom Cupboard

MILDRED *and* MAUD *are still trying to escape from the cupboard.* MILDRED *desperately flings herself against the door –*

– And falls out as ENID *opens it.* TABBY *is with her.*

MILDRED Enid!

ENID Hey guys.

MAUD How did you know we were here?

ENID Tabby came to get me. What's up, witches?

MILDRED *and* MAUD *fall over themselves trying to warn her:*

MILDRED Miss Cackle's evil / twin

MAUD / twin is trying to take /

MILDRED / MAUD Over the school!

ENID Awesome! Can't believe I nearly slept through this!

MAUD Come on. We need to help her!

ENID Yeah we do… Which one are we helping again?

MILDRED AND MAUD Miss Cackle!

The three of them sneak along the corridor together…

Corridor by Miss Cackle's Study

MILDRED, MAUD *and* **ENID** *listen at the door.*

MAUD They're in there! Both of them!

ENID What's going on? Are they fighting?

MAUD Seems like they're – talking... I can't hear what they're saying!

MILDRED I know! We could send Tabby in!

TABBY *(mews plaintively)*

MILDRED I know it's scary! But we need to know what's happening in there.

TABBY *mews and sneaks through the door.*

Thank you, Tabby...

Corridor / Miss Cackle's Study

MILDRED, MAUD *and* ENID *huddle close,* MILDRED *concentrating as she tries to see through* TABBY*'s eyes –* *"Tabby-cam".* TABBY *sneaks into the study and watches as* MISS CACKLE *(by means of a double!) confronts* AGATHA.

AGATHA *and* MISS CACKLE *are taking tea and buns.*

AGATHA Only you would invite your conqueror for tea and buns.

MISS CACKLE We're sisters, after all. I see no reason not to be civil. Crumpet?

AGATHA I'll take your crumpet. Then I'll take your school.

MISS CACKLE Yes dear, that's what you always say.

MILDRED*'s watching and listening through* TABBY. MAUD *nudges her.*

MAUD What's happening?

MILDRED They're having tea.

ENID Tea with your evil twin. Awks.

MISS CACKLE How did you manage to break through my protective spells, by the way?

AGATHA Your spells failed. On Hallowe'en, of all nights. You're slipping, Sister. All that goodness must have addled your brain. It's time you retired, and gave me *my* school.

MISS CACKLE You're the one whose brain is addled. The school has always been mine.

AGATHA Because you're three minutes older than me! Three minutes! That's all!

MISS CACKLE For the Grand High Witch's sake, Agatha, how many times? It was because you're *evil*!

AGATHA You mean strong. Tough. Taking back control. Making witching great again.

MISS CACKLE   Evil.

> *A furious* **AGATHA** *overturns the table. At the noise,* **TABBY** *jumps down and runs to* **MILDRED**.

MAUD   *(re. table falling)* Did you hear that?!

MILDRED   Tabby! Are you OK?

TABBY   *(mews, pathetic, scared)*

MILDRED   They *are* fighting!

ENID   Awesome, I've always wanted to see a witch-fight.

MILDRED   *(to* **TABBY***)* Who's winning?

> **TABBY** *just mews plaintively again…*

> *Up in* **MISS CACKLE***'s office, the double sneaks away and now one actor is playing both parts, using split costume so that the left profile is* **AGATHA** *and the right profile is* **MISS CACKLE**.

AGATHA   Say that to me one more time. I dare you!

MISS CACKLE   Evil. Evil. Evil. And you know what they say about evil twins.

AGATHA   People will say anything.

MISS CACKLE   They say there's something rotten in their soul.

AGATHA   That is just the way I roll.

MISS CACKLE   *(sings)*
THEY SAY THAT SOMETIMES, IN A MOTHER'S WOMB,
TWO TINY PEOPLE, FIGHTING FOR ROOM,
SOMETHING TWISTS AND EVERYTHING GOES WRONG…

AGATHA   *(sings)*
WHY ARE YOU TALKING SO LONG?

MISS CACKLE
A PERSONALITY IS SPLIT.

AGATHA

BUT NEITHER SIDE WILL EVER QUIT.

MISS CACKLE

SO EVERYTHING GOOD GOES – HERE, AND THE BAD GOES –
THERE.

AGATHA

LET'S JUST TALK ABOUT WHERE.

MISS CACKLE

EVIL TWIN...

AGATHA

IF YOU REALLY WANT TO THINK THAT...

MISS CACKLE

EVIL TWIN...

AGATHA

BUT IT REALLY, REALLY STINKS THAT YOU WON'T GIVE ME A
CHANCE, AND YOU NEVER WOULD.

MISS CACKLE

I WOULD IF I COULD!
JUST GIVE IT UP.
THE SCHOOL IS MINE, NOW—

AGATHA

YOU'VE HAD YOUR TIME, NOW –
IT'S AGATHA'S TURN—

MISS CACKLE

WHEN WILL YOU EVER LEARN?
MOTHER TRUSTED ME.

AGATHA

NO, SHE JUST DIDN'T SEE.
THAT YOU'RE NOT FIT TO RULE.

MISS CACKLE

PLEASE LEAVE MY SCHOOL.
I NEVER DID THIS TO YOU.
YOU ARE MY SISTER TOO.
AND I DON'T WANT TO HURT YOU—

AGATHA

WELL THE FEELING'S NOT MUTUAL!
'COS I JUST WANT TO BOOT YOU ALL!

The **GIRLS** *join in as backing singers and dancers.*

GIRLS

GIVE IT UP.

AGATHA

BEFORE IT'S TOO LATE.

GIRLS

GIVE IT UP.

AGATHA

OR BEWARE YOUR FATE.

GIRLS

GIVE IT UP.

MISS CACKLE

I JUST WANT TO HELP.

GIRLS

GIVE IT UP.

MISS CACKLE

BEFORE YOU HURT YOURSELF.

GIRLS

GIVE IT UP.

MISS CACKLE

LET ME PROTECT YOU.

GIRLS

GIVE IT UP.

AGATHA

YEAH, LIKE I'D LET YOU.

GIRLS

GIVE IT UP.

MISS CACKLE
GIVE IT UP!

GIRLS
GIVE IT UP.

AGATHA
GIVE IT UP!

ALL
GIVE IT UP!.

The number builds to a crescendo and dance break, and ends with **AGATHA** *triumphant:*

AGATHA
GIVE IT UP!

The song ends. The backing singers and dancers leave. **MISS CACKLE** *is still humming and tapping her toes...*

MISS CACKLE
GIVE IT UP...

Looks around.

Sorry dear, which of us is talking now?

AGATHA *Me!* Ada, you've lost. I've already snailed one of the girls. You won't let me hurt any more and you know it. You're too damn *nice*. So just hand over the keys and leave quietly...

MAUD *and* **ENID** *bravely run in and distract* **AGATHA** *while* **MILDRED** *sneaks round behind her.*

MAUD Don't worry Miss Cackle! We're here to help you.

ENID *(seeing the snail)* Is that Ethel?

AGATHA How did you know?

ENID Looks just like her.

AGATHA *raises her arms threateningly.* **MILDRED** *is sneaking up on her.*

AGATHA Well, you'll all look like that in a minute.

She points at **MILDRED** *behind her back.*

And don't think I haven't seen you there, girl!

AGATHA's *magic grabs* **MILDRED** *by the plait and drags her in front of* **AGATHA**.

TABBY *(mews)*

MILDRED Tabby, no!

Action sequence: slow motion. **TABBY** *leaps onto* **AGATHA**'s *face.* **AGATHA** *clutches at her face, removes* **TABBY** *and throws him at* **MAUD**, *who throws him to* **ENID**.

AGATHA Throw your cat at me, would you? Prepare to be mollusced!

AGATHA *throws a spell at* **MILDRED**. **FENELLA** *carries a 'lightning spark' representing the spell, which travels in slow motion from* **AGATHA** *to* **MAUD**.

Seeing that **AGATHA**'s *spell is about to hit* **MILDRED**, **MAUD** *throws herself in front of* **MILDRED** *to protect her...*

MAUD Milllll-drrrrr-ed!

...And reacts as the spell REBOUNDS from her glasses, **FENELLA** *carries the spark back and it hits* **AGATHA**, *who staggers around and collapses...*

...And **MISS CACKLE** *stands up. Holding an* **AGATHA**-*snail.*

MISS CACKLE Hooray. Oh, well done, girls. Very well done.

MAUD What happened?

MISS CACKLE My sister's spell rebounded off your glasses. Useful things, glasses.

MAUD *(looks at the snail)* What about Ethel?

MISS CACKLE Oh, yes. Ethel.

MISS CACKLE *makes a magical gesture, the* ETHEL-*snail vanishes and* ETHEL *appears. (Perhaps with some comedy antennae?)*

ETHEL This doesn't change anything! Mildred still deserves to be expelled!

DRUSILLA *enters.*

DRUSILLA No, she doesn't. I told them what you did—

MISS HARDBROOM *appears.*

MISS HARDBROOM *What* is going on here?

MISS CACKLE Oh, nothing to worry about, Hecate. All you need to know is that our school is safe. Thanks to these brave, clever girls – no actually, that's enough, I'm even making myself want to vomit.

MISS CACKLE *takes off her cardigan/wig and reveals that she's really* AGATHA.

ETHEL *(turns to "*MISS CACKLE*" who is really* AGATHA*)* Is it over? Can we finally drop this ridiculous charade?

ENID What's she on about?

MILDRED *is staring at* MISS CACKLE / AGATHA – *realising...*

MILDRED Oh, no...

AGATHA *(smiles at* MILDRED, *evil)* Oh, yes...

MISS HARDBROOM *picks up the costume elements that* AGATHA *dropped. Studies them. Thinking hard...*

ETHEL Agatha, are the spells ready?

AGATHA Yes. They have been for ages.

ETHEL And you still made me suffer through that vile play! Why didn't you make your move earlier?

AGATHA What, and miss my big number?

ENID So...she's *Agatha*? Like, real, actual Agatha?

MILDRED Yes.

MAUD *grabs her cans and gabbles into them:*

MAUD Mavis! We've got a problem. Potential show stop—

AGATHA *blasts* MAUD *with magic. The cans explode and* MAUD *drops them.*

MILDRED ...I should have known...

MAUD *(to* AGATHA*)* What have you done with the real Miss Cackle?

MISS HARDBROOM *(to* AGATHA*)* I do hope you haven't done anything reckless.

AGATHA I haven't killed her, if that's what you mean. Not yet. I've got big plans for Big Sis.

ETHEL*'s been dying to boast of her cleverness.*

ETHEL I got rid of her at the interval.

DRUSILLA *(shocked) You* did?

ETHEL Funny she never saw it coming. Seeing as I'm *such* a bully.

MISS HARDBROOM You were her student. She trusted you.

ETHEL She always did underestimate me.

AGATHA My dear sister didn't suspect a thing – until it was too late. And then...I took over.

MAUD But *why*? What do you even *want*? Oh, of course...

AGATHA The school—

MAUD / ENID / MILDRED / DRUSILLA *(simultaneously, with* AGATHA*)* The school.

AGATHA Let me finish! The school – is only the start! Imagine this... Band, dramatic music if you please.

The **BAND**, *with zombie-like expressions, start to play dramatic music.*

MAUD You don't have to do what she says!

ETHEL Yes they do. I slipped a little Obedience potion into their water bottles.

ENID So the dragonsbane *was* yours.

AGATHA *Getting back* to my plans for world domination—

MILDRED *(shocked) World* domination?

AGATHA *Thank* you, *that's* the reaction I'm looking for. Now, imagine this...

The **BAND** *play suitably intense music.*

A glorious empire, lasting forever. Based on good, old-fashioned values. The plebs kept in line by fear and superstition. A world ruled by witches. And by witches, I mean me.

MISS HARDBROOM And how do you intend to achieve all this?

AGATHA I shall absorb my sister's powers, combine them with my own, take over the Academy – then – the world!

MISS HARDBROOM One has to admire your ambition. But really, Agatha, *must* you involve the Academy in this?

AGATHA The Academy is vital to my plot! It's a potential powerhouse of thaumaturgical force.

Apart from **ETHEL**, *the* **GIRLS** *look blank.*

ETHEL *(explains smugly)* Magical energy.

AGATHA When enough witches work together, they can achieve the unthinkable. Channelling morphic resonance through two hundred powerful young minds, we will control the physical world as well as the minds of everyone on Earth!

MILDRED *(to* **MISS HARDBROOM***)* She can't do that – can she?

MISS HARDBROOM The thaumaturgical theory is sound...

AGATHA Join me, Hecate. Together, we will build a world fit for witches.

MILDRED No!

ENID Come on, HB!

MAUD Miss Hardbroom, you can't!

> **MISS HARDBROOM** *holds up a hand; the* **GIRLS** *instantly fall silent.*

MISS HARDBROOM *(to* **AGATHA***)* All right, you've convinced me. I'm in.

DRUSILLA *(shocked)* Miss Hardbroom!

FENELLA No!

ENID No way, HB!

AGATHA Silence, brats!

> *To the* **BAND**.

Not you!

> *The* **BAND** *play on.*

Well, well, well, Hecate Hardbroom. I thought you were loyal to my sister.

MISS HARDBROOM My loyalty is pledged to the Craft, the Academy and the Cackle family. In that order. As the Code tells us, witches must act in the best interests of all witches.

MILDRED But Agatha's *evil*!

MISS HARDBROOM Evil is just a point of view.

> *To* **AGATHA**.

And from where I'm standing, your sister has been letting things slip.

> *At* **ENID**.

Admitting disruptive students.

At **MILDRED.**

Accepting lower standards in the name of so-called diversity.

MAUD *(indignant)* Miss Cackle's a brilliant headmistress. And you're supposed to be her best friend!

MISS HARDBROOM Witches don't make friends. Only convenient alliances.

Looking at **AGATHA, MISS HARDBROOM** *touches her forehead in a gesture of respect.*

Agatha.

AGATHA Hecate.

The two of them share an elaborate witchy handshake.

MILDRED Noooo!

ENID You can't do this!

FENELLA Miss Hardbroom, don't!

MISS HARDBROOM Quiet! I know what I'm doing. This is the best way, for all of us. *Trust me.*

The **GIRLS** *glance at each other – does* **MISS HARDBROOM** *have a secret plan?*

AGATHA Good. Let's get on with it.

AGATHA *gestures to* **ETHEL,** *who gestures brusquely to* **DRUSILLA***:*

ETHEL Drusilla!

DRUSILLA *follows* **ETHEL** *off.*

MISS HARDBROOM *(to* **AGATHA***)* You said you planned to absorb Ada's powers – what have you done with her?

AGATHA To be honest, I've been dying to tell someone. It's rather amusing. But first, let us dress for the occasion!

ETHEL and **DRUSILLA** *bring on a shiny, glittering case containing long, hooded robes and hand them to* **AGATHA** *and* **MISS HARDBROOM**.

MISS HARDBROOM *(to* **AGATHA***)* Those are the Grand High Witch's robes.

AGATHA As of now, *I* am the Grand High Witch. And you are the Supreme Sorceress. If you will accept that honour.

MISS HARDBROOM A little flashy for me, but I do like the stitching. Must have taken you ages.

Having handed over the robes, **ETHEL** *gestures to* **DRUSILLA** *to follow her offstage – for their next task...*

AGATHA I had plenty of time. All those years in exile—

MILDRED You were doing embroidery?

AGATHA Yes, and plotting my revenge!

MISS HARDBROOM You do realise that absorbing another witch's powers will require a substantial amount of magical energy.

AGATHA Duh! But I'm ready. I've been waiting for this moment all my life.

MISS HARDBROOM *(sotto)* Don't panic girls. Stay with me.

AGATHA *makes a magical gesture. Darkness falls as* **ETHEL** *and* **DRUSILLA** *bring the mirror onto the stage.*

As the witches all stare at the mirror, a face appears in it. It's **MISS CACKLE**. *She screams silently and claws at the front of the mirror, trying to escape.*

MAUD She's trapped in the mirror!

MAUD, **ENID** *and* **MILDRED** *huddle close to* **MISS HARDBROOM**.

AGATHA *(to* MISS CACKLE *in the mirror)* Look, Sister! Even your most devoted follower has betrayed you. Miss Hardbroom is on my side now. Aren't you, Miss Hardbroom—

Notices MISS HARDBROOM *making a magical gesture.*

Wait, what are you doing? No!

ETHEL She's tricking you! She's trying to free Miss Cackle.

AGATHA No! No!

Cracks begin to appear in the mirror and MISS CACKLE *(in the mirror) begins to tap on the surface...*

Hardbroom, I might have known you'd betray me!

MISS HARDBROOM As if I would ever break the Witches' Code!

AGATHA *(explodes)* Enough about the stupid Code!

AGATHA *blasts* MISS HARDBROOM *with magic.* MISS HARDBROOM*'s robes fall to the ground as she vanishes.*

MILDRED Miss Hardbroom!

ENID *(simultaneously)* HB!

FENELLA / DRUSILLA Aargh!

As MISS HARDBROOM *vanishes, the cracks in the mirror disappear and the mirror goes blank.*

ETHEL *goes over to the fallen cloak and pulls out a small book...*

ETHEL *(reading the front)* The Witches' Code—

AGATHA She lived her life by the book.

ETHEL *opens the book and* MISS HARDBROOM*'s disembodied voice comes out:*

MISS HARDBROOM *(from the book)* Ethel, it's not too late. You don't have to go through with—

ETHEL *slams the book shut.*

AGATHA   Well, Hardbroom turned out to be quite the disappointment. Anyone else feeling disloyal?

The GIRLS *glance at each other, trying to get up the courage to defy her.*

Good. Then pledge allegiance to your new Headmistress – soon to be Head of the whole world!

ENID   *(can't help herself)* You are joking us.

MAUD   *(quick, nervous)* Enid!

ENID   I'm sorry, but what? Her, the dictator of the world?

To AGATHA.

Seriously, get over yourself.

AGATHA   My mighty deeds shall shake the very foundations of the universe.

ENID   What, like that time you snailed yourself in your sister's office?

AGATHA*'s face distorts in fury at the memory.*

AGATHA   That – did not – happen.

MAUD   It did, actually.

ENID   Totally did.

MILDRED   We all saw it.

ENID   We've been laughing about it for the last four years.

AGATHA   *(furious)* Four years—!

Then, controlling herself.

It doesn't matter. There were no witnesses—

ENID / MAUD / MILDRED   There were! Yeah, us, we saw it! *(etc.)*

AGATHA   No *living* witnesses, anyway.

MAUD, ENID *and* MILDRED *look at each other and suddenly realise their danger.*

ENID Run!

ENID, MAUD, MILDRED *and* FENELLA *run away in different directions.*

AGATHA Come back here! Stop! I will destroy you!

The furious AGATHA *throws spell after spell at the fleeing* GIRLS. ENID, MAUD *and* MILDRED *manage to dodge the spells, but* AGATHA*'s spells hit the set, which partially falls down. A light falls and is caught on a safety bar. It's chaos.*

AGATHA *casts a spell, magically dragging* FENELLA *back onto the stage and dragging some set and props too, including a potions desk.*

They won't get far. This whole theatre is spellbound. No witch can leave.

ETHEL *(to* FENELLA*)* Stay there. Don't try to run away again.

FENELLA Why are you doing this? It can't just be about Mildred Hubble—

ETHEL It's *not* about Mildred Hubble! I'm backing Agatha because I believe in her vision. I want to make witching great again.

To ETHEL*'s shock,* ENID *suddenly pops up from behind the mirror.*

ENID Nah, you just did it 'cos you've got no mates!

ETHEL *(startled)* That's not true!

ENID It is, you know. Even Agatha's only using you.

ETHEL Liar!

ETHEL *throws a spell at* ENID. ENID *grabs the shiny case the robes came in, and deflects it back at* ETHEL. ETHEL *finds herself choking – but* **AGATHA** *comes to her rescue. She makes magical gestures and frees* **ETHEL** *from her choking attack.*

AGATHA That was careless, Ethel.

ETHEL Sorry.

AGATHA Well, no harm done. Want me to turn her into a skunk? Or a toilet seat?

ETHEL *wiggles her fingers, "limbering up" for a magical battle.*

ETHEL Don't bother. I've got this one.

AGATHA Then prove yourself.

ETHEL Just watch me.

ENID Bring it, witch!

ENID *and* **ETHEL** *throw spells at each other.* **ENID** *is agile, dodging* **ETHEL**'s *spells cleverly, ducking behind bits of set.* **ENID** *hits* **ETHEL** *with an itching spell, a sneezing spell and a spell which makes* **ETHEL** *snort like a pig (again).*

Finally, a furious **ETHEL** *gains control. She stretches* **ENID**'s *tongue out so that it's impossibly long, and gains control over her. She puts the robe case on the potions desk, drags* **ENID** *inside the case, hammering her down into a seemingly impossible space.* **ETHEL** *slams down the lid and sits on it – victor at last.*

ETHEL *(exhausted but triumphant)* I've always wanted to do that.

ETHEL *moves the case down from the desk.*

AGATHA One witness down, two to go.

ETHEL There they are!

ETHEL *spots* MILDRED *and* MAUD *trying to escape in the auditorium. A back door flips open and shut.*

AGATHA Mildred Hubble!

AGATHA *fires a magical blast at* MILDRED *but misses.*

(to the audience) There she is! Get her! I said, *get her*! Listen to your future leader! Bring me Mildred Hubble! I warn you, don't think of helping her to escape. If you do, there will be *painful* consequences.

AGATHA *picks up the* TABBY *puppet. Slowly and deliberately, she tears it apart.*

(to the audience) Come on! It's a glove. It hasn't even got any eyes! Really? Well, if *that* bothers you so much, just wait until I get my hands on the *real thing*. That mangy little moggy will be toast! And so will its owner.

And as for all of *you* – give Mildred Hubble up now, and maybe I won't turn you all into frogs!

Who is hiding her? Is it you? How dare you defy me? *Bring – me – Mildred – Hubble!*

With each word, AGATHA *points at a different part of the auditorium and blasts out a spell. An usher's ice creams explode. Programmes are blasted everywhere.*

"MILDRED" *appears in the audience.*

MILDRED Stop it! Don't hurt anyone else! I give up. I surrender.

AGATHA Come here, Mildred. Come on. I promise I won't hurt you. As long as you promise to be on *my* side.

MILDRED All right...

"MILDRED" *appears on stage and slowly walks towards* AGATHA. AGATHA *throws a magical lasso and catches her.* "MILDRED" *falls to the floor and is slowly "dragged" towards* AGATHA.

AGATHA Gotcha, you little worm!

"MILDRED" You promised—

AGATHA Promises made to plebs don't count!

> AGATHA *attacks* "MILDRED" *with magic.* "MILDRED"
> *tries to resist but is no match for her. They make no
> contact throughout, but* AGATHA *throws vicious spells
> at* MILDRED, *who is obviously in distress. Even* ETHEL
> *is appalled:*

ETHEL *(to* AGATHA*)* What are you doing?

AGATHA Dissent cannot be tolerated. All witches must be of
one mind.

> AGATHA *throws a final spell – and* "MILDRED" *lies still.*

> DRUSILLA, FENELLA *and* ETHEL *are all shocked, can't
> believe what's just happened.*

> ETHEL *indicates* "MILDRED"*'s body.*

ETHEL Is she – did you...is she...?

AGATHA I did what must be done.

> AGATHA *walks aside, coolly examining her fingers after
> the witching battle.*

Tch! The little horror made me break a nail.

> DRUSILLA, FENELLA *and* ETHEL *all look in horror at*
> "MILDRED"*'s body. The others won't meet* ETHEL*'s eyes.*
> ETHEL *goes over to* AGATHA.

ETHEL Can we do something to help her? It's not too late – is it?

AGATHA Oh, don't you go all snowflake on me now.

> AGATHA *gestures to* DRUSILLA *and* FENELLA. *They
> bring on a cloth and cover up* "MILDRED"*'s body.*

(to ETHEL*)* You can't take over the world without a little collateral damage. Surely you knew that?

ETHEL *(to* AGATHA*)* I just – didn't think it would go this far.

AGATHA Then you didn't think at all. Think now, Ethel Hallow. And think fast. Whose side are you on?

ETHEL *(thinks. Honestly)* Mine.

AGATHA *considers this – then smiles.*

AGATHA Spoken like a true witch. I think you'll make an excellent sidekick.

ETHEL *Sidekick...?*

Then, meek.

Yes, of course. Your sidekick. That's what I am.

DRUSILLA *and* FENELLA *are shocked.*

DRUSILLA You can't work for her! After what she just did—

AGATHA *strides back over to* DRUSILLA, *threatening:*

AGATHA You will *all* work for me! Unless you want to end up like—

AGATHA *pulls the cloth back from* "MILDRED"*'s body dramatically – to reveal the body of* MAUD.

ETHEL *Maud??*

AGATHA *(looks round, bewildered)* Where's Mildred Hubble?

ETHEL *(realising)* Maud must have used a Looky-Likey Spell.

DRUSILLA Like you did. She got the idea from you.

ETHEL *thinks about this...*

AGATHA You can't hide from me, Mildred Hubble. Wherever you are, I will find you...

ETHEL *(suddenly points, dramatically, to the back of the auditorium)* There she goes! Look! She's trying to run away—

AGATHA Wait there. This one's all mine.

> AGATHA *storms off through the auditorium (threatening audience members on the way). When she's gone,* ETHEL *looks up.*

ETHEL It's all right. She's gone. For now.

> MILDRED *climbs down from above.*

MILDRED *(to* ETHEL*)* Thank you.

ETHEL *(quiet, gutted)* Don't.

> MILDRED *goes over to* MAUD*'s body and stands looking at her.*

MILDRED *(of* MAUD*)* She thought she was saving me...

ETHEL I know.

> *For a moment, the two* GIRLS *look at* MAUD*'s body – equally devastated.* FENELLA *and* DRUSILLA *join them:*

DRUSILLA *(sad, desperate)* What do we do now?

ETHEL There's nothing we can do against Agatha's magic.

MILDRED There has to be. We have to stop her.

> *Gathering strength.*

We owe it to Maud. There must be someone who can help –

> *To* ETHEL*.*

What about your family? Your sisters and your mum?

ETHEL Them? They won't help us.

MILDRED But we're all in mortal danger—

ETHEL And *I'm* a *Hallow*! Oh, I wouldn't expect you to understand. I suppose *your* mother would come running here to save you if she could.

MILDRED Of course she would.

ETHEL That's the difference between us. *My* mother says, others may sink or swim. But a Hallow always floats. Lifebelts are for losers. She wouldn't help me and I wouldn't ask.

MILDRED She sounds horrible.

ETHEL She's a Level Thirteen witch! And you...are nothing. You come from nowhere. You're nobody... *(beat)* You're so lucky.

MILDRED You mean, all this time...*you* were jealous of *me*?

ETHEL Jealous? A Hallow jealous of *you*? Don't make me laugh.

ETHEL tries to laugh, but can't.

DRUSILLA Guys, Agatha will be back soon. We need a plan.

ETHEL I know!

MILDRED Where's Enid?

A beat. **DRUSILLA** *snitches:*

DRUSILLA She's in the suitcase—

ETHEL I'm sorry, OK!

ETHEL makes a magical gesture, undoing her spell.
DRUSILLA and FENELLA help ENID out of the desk.

MILDRED Enid!

ENID I'm back, witches!

But her face falls as she sees MAUD's body.

What happened? Maud—?

MILDRED Maud saved me. And now we have to save the world without her. Starting with Miss Cackle.

Glances at the magic mirror.

(to ETHEL*)* How do we get her out?

ETHEL We can't. Agatha's magic trapped her in the mirror! She's more powerful than any of us.

MILDRED But is she more powerful than *all* of us?

FENELLA What do you mean?

MILDRED Remember what Miss Bat said?

ETHEL No. Who listens to that shrivelled old hag?

ENID I did! She said, we can magnify our power by working together.

MILDRED *(looking at the mirror, sings quietly)*
HOLD THE CIRCLE...

More confident.

HOLD THE CIRCLE...

ENID *joins in.*

MILDRED / ENID
HOLD THE CIRCLE EVERMORE...

ETHEL, FENELLA *and* DRUSILLA *join in, forming a circle.*

ETHEL / ENID / FENELLA / DRUSILLA
HOLD THE CIRCLE, HOLD THE CIRCLE,
HOLD THE CIRCLE EVERMORE.

ALL *the* GIRLS, *including the* HYPNOTISED BAND, *join in.*

ALL
HOLD THE CIRCLE, HOLD THE CIRCLE,
HOLD THE CIRCLE, HOLD THE CIRCLE.

MILDRED It's not enough! We need more!

ENID *(gestures to audience)* What about them?

ETHEL Them? They're plebs!

To the audience.

Sorry. I mean – normals.

MILDRED I'm normal! But I still learned to do magic.

ETHEL If you say so.

MILDRED What if it doesn't matter who your parents are? What if *everyone* is a – a potential powerhouse of thaumaturgical force!

ETHEL No. Witches are different. Witches are special. Witches are *better*.

MILDRED If I can be a witch, anyone can!

To the audience.

Come on. We can do this. Together.

MILDRED / ENID
JOIN THE CIRCLE, JOIN THE CIRCLE.

The **BAND** *are released from their trance.*

MISS BAT Come on everyone, sing up!

MISS DRILL Give it some welly!

The **BAND** *joins in:*

ALL
JOIN THE CIRCLE, JOIN THE CIRCLE,
JOIN THE CIRCLE. JOIN THE CIRCLE!

ETHEL It's working... But they're nothing but a bunch of oiks... And some of them are *boys*!

ENID So what? Who says boys can't be witches?

ETHEL Everyone!

ENID *(ignoring* **ETHEL**. *To boys in audience)* Come on guys, we need all the help we can get!

When I say join, you say circle!

Join – circle! Join – circle.

ALL

> JOIN THE CIRCLE, JOIN THE CIRCLE,
> JOIN THE CIRCLE. JOIN THE CIRCLE!

> *The* **GIRLS** *chant, in a circle focusing on the mirror. And with a sudden magical flash...*

> *...***MISS HARDBROOM** *appears and joins the circle – much to the* **GIRLS***' surprise.*

MILDRED Oh. Miss Hardbroom.

ENID Nice one, guys! It worked.

MILDRED Sort of.

MISS HARDBROOM I suppose it would be too much to ask for you to be pleased to see me.

> **AGATHA***'s voice booms out:*

AGATHA Back off, Hardbroom! Resistance is useless.

> **AGATHA** *forces* **MISS HARDBROOM** *back and magically binds her to the set. The* **BAND** *revert to playing* **AGATHA***'s dramatic music.*

I was always more powerful than you, Hecate. And now, I am now a Level Fifteen witch.

ENID You can't be. The levels only go up to thirteen.

AGATHA I made up two more, that's how good I am.

> **AGATHA** *taps on the mirror.* **MISS CACKLE** *appears inside.*

Well, hello, Sister. It's me. The evil one. Apparently. And as we know, there's only one cure for evil twin syndrome.

MISS HARDBROOM No!

AGATHA I won't just absorb my sister's powers. I will absorb *her.*

MISS HARDBROOM You can't! It will destroy both of you!

MILDRED Please! Don't hurt Miss Cackle!

AGATHA Oh, she won't feel a thing. Except the searing agony as I absorb her powers, her knowledge and her very soul.

MISS HARDBROOM Agatha, don't be a fool! No twin has ever survived the reintegration process.

AGATHA Level Fifteen, remember? See you on the other side, girls...

AGATHA moves towards the mirror – and as she touches it there's an explosion. AGATHA *moves inside the mirror. As she does so,* MISS HARDBROOM *is freed.*

A struggle. AGATHA *and* MISS CACKLE *merge. The mirror cracks. One being steps out – is this* AGATHA *or* MISS CACKLE*?*

MILDRED She's OK!

MISS HARDBROOM *One* of them is.

Various emotions and expressions – good and evil, happy and painful – pass across MISS CACKLE's *face before she gains control of herself enough to gasp:*

MISS CACKLE *(to* MISS HARDBROOM*)* Hecate!

MISS HARDBROOM *runs to her side.*

MISS HARDBROOM Ada? Is that you?

MISS CACKLE *(her face still contorting)* I... I... I want... I deserve... I need... I will destroy – I could really – *murder* – a nice cup of tea and a bun. Yes. With pink icing and a cherry on top.

ENID It's her. I'll get the buns!

Runs off for tea and buns.

MILDRED Miss Cackle, please – *(gestures to the fallen* MAUD*)* Maud...

MISS CACKLE Oh, my goodness.

MISS HARDBROOM What happened here?

MISS CACKLE, with an air of examining the patient, feels the air around MAUD, detecting magic:

MISS CACKLE Agatha's work. I'm so sorry, dear.

MILDRED Can you help her? Please. You have to.

MISS CACKLE What magic has done, magic can undo. But I'll need your help, girls. Hecate.

MISS HARDBROOM Ada.

MISS CACKLE, MISS HARDBROOM and the GIRLS form a magical circle around MAUD.

Their powers combine to create a powerful force. Bits of set restore themselves to their original positions.

MISS CACKLE Time to wake up now, Maud.

MAUD wakes up.

MAUD Miss Cackle... Miss Hardbroom... Millie.

MILDRED Maud.

MILDRED and MAUD hug. Emotional.

ENID enters with tea and buns.

ENID Got your tea, Miss C – oh, hey, Maud.

MAUD Hey, Enid.

ENID Looks like everything worked out all right again. Bun?

MAUD Yes please, I'm starving.

MISS CACKLE takes her tea. MAUD grabs a bun.

ETHEL Stop it! Everything's not all right.

MISS CACKLE *(grave)* Yes, Ethel. What have you to say for yourself?

ETHEL I'm sorry. I'm sorry I sided with Agatha, and everything that happened...it was all my fault.

MISS CACKLE That's it? No excuses? No trying to pin the blame on anyone else?

ETHEL *shakes her head.*

ETHEL No.

MISS HARDBROOM That might just possibly be the strangest thing that has happened today.

MILDRED I just want to say – Ethel didn't realise what Agatha would do – and we couldn't have saved everyone without her.

MISS CACKLE You always try to see the good in everyone, don't you, Mildred? I think that's an excellent quality in a Head Girl.

MILDRED *turns to* **MISS CACKLE** *in shock.*

MILDRED Head Girl?

And indeed, **MILDRED** *looks down to see a gleaming Head Girl badge pinned to her uniform!*

I don't believe it!

MAUD I do!

ENID Well done, Mildred!

MAUD *and* **ENID** *hug* **MILDRED**.

MISS CACKLE As these girls move into their fifth and final year, I can only hope that our new recruits will live up to their standard.

To the audience.

Who knows? It seems that witching powers can be found in the most unlikely places.

Maybe even...in one of you here tonight.

MISS HARDBROOM Mildred. I think somebody wishes to congratulate you.

MISS HARDBROOM *picks up the broken* **TABBY** *glove puppet, puts it into a cauldron and waves her hand over the top in a magical gesture. The broken puppet magically becomes a lovely new cat. She hands it to* **MILDRED.**

MILDRED Tabby!

MAUD *(on cans)* Mavis, go finale!

ALL *(sing)*
ONWARD, EVER STRIVING ONWARD
PROUDLY ON OUR BROOMS WE FLY
STRAIGHT AND TRUE ABOVE THE TREE TOPS
SHADOWS ON THE MOONLIT SKY.
NEVER A DAY WILL PASS BEFORE US
WHEN WE HAVEN'T TRIED OUR BEST
KEPT OUR CAULDRONS BUBBLING NICELY
CAST OUR SPELLS AND CHARMS WITH ZEST.

OOOH... DON'T YOU KNOW THAT WE'RE THE WITCHING KIND?
OOOH... DON'T YOU KNOW THAT WE'RE THE WITCHING KIND?

DOUBLE DOUBLE TOIL AND TROUBLE
FIRE BURN AND CAULDRON BUBBLE
FILLET OF A FENNY SNAKE
IN THE CAULDRON BOIL AND BAKE
EYE OF NEWT AND TOE OF FROG
WOOL OF BAT AND TONGUE OF DOG
ADDER'S FORK AND BLIND-WORM'S STING
LIZARD'S LEG AND HOWLET'S WING
FOR A CHARM OF POWERFUL TROUBLE
LIKE A HELL-BROTH BOIL AND BUBBLE
DOUBLE DOUBLE TOIL AND TROUBLE
FIRE BURN AND CAULDRON BUBBLE
COOL IT WITH A BABOON'S BLOOD
THEN THE CHARM IS FIRM AND GOOD.
DOUBLE DOUBLE TOIL AND TROUBLE

FIRE BURN AND CAULDRON –
DOUBLE DOUBLE TOIL AND TROUBLE
FIRE BURN AND CAULDRON BUBBLE
WE'RE THE WITCHING KIND!
DON'T YOU KNOW WE'RE THE WITCHING KIND?
DON'T YOU KNOW, DON'T YOU KNOW WE'RE THE WITCHING
    KIND?
DON'T YOU KNOW WE'RE THE WITCHING KIND?
DON'T YOU KNOW, DON'T YOU KNOW WE'RE THE WITCHING
    KIND?
DON'T YOU KNOW WE'RE THE WITCHING KIND?
DON'T YOU KNOW, DON'T YOU KNOW WE'RE THE WITCHING
    KIND?
DON'T YOU KNOW WE'RE THE WITCHING KIND?

PROPERTY LIST

ACT 1

PRESET ONSTAGE
Curtains closed
Set in position 1 (red)
2 x roll up banners (DSL and DSR) – photos on onstage sides
Miss Cackle's Academy banner hung
Broomstick
Check potion bottles over LEDs

MUSIC CORNER
MISS DRILL's broom
ENID – mic
FENELLA – witches hat (WARDROBE)
FENELLA –Tabby glove on shelf

DS POTIONS SHELVES
2 x additional potion bottles for **ETHEL**

DORMITORY PLATFORM
6 x exercise books on US side of top step

ON STAIRS TO MISS CACKLE'S OFFICE
6 x sashes in black box (WARDROBE)

STAGE LEFT
Scooter – resting against pros wall DS
MILDRED satchel with city road academy brochure inside. Placed over handle of scooter
US of 2nd masker:
   - **MAUD** suitcase (owls) and cat basket-with blue collar cat, and black body inside
   - **ETHEL** suitcase (purple) and cat basket - with Nightstar cat (ON), and black body inside
MAUD *and* **MILDRED**'s *potions desk: Set against Prompt corner*
   - Set with all potions items. Including 2 x green test tubes without lids
   - Invisibility cloths in drawer with 2 x opera gloves set ready to put on. R-H glove on SL side, L-H glove on SR side.
   - 2 x Tabby feet (B), 1 x tabby glove (D) R-H in drawer
DRUSILLA and **FENELLA**'s potions desk: Set US of M+M desk
   - Magic desk

- Set with all potions items. Including 2 x green test tubes without lids
MILDRED city road academy uniform (WARDROBE)

Mirror: Set US of prompt corner
- **AGATHA** sparkly dress hanging on rail, shoes behind cloaks
3 x standard brooms
MILDRED's whole broom (2nd in from SR on rack)
ENID nightrider broom
Broken broom
4 x hats (WARDROBE)

Trunk:
- Mirror and cloaks inside
Head girl badge
2 x mobile phones
Door knob
Drill
Clipboard with pencil
Comms headset and pack
AGATHA black Maglite (CHECK WORKING)
MAUD glasses
4 x witches code books
2 x band water bottles (Clean and full of drinking water. CHECK WORKING)
2 x cat feet.
1 x tabby glove.
1 x tabby sleeve.
Small snail
Pair of blue gloves
Pile of mother moon scores
Test tube

Cat collection point:
- sleeve and glove (R-H)
- sleeve
MISS CACKLE phone and witches code book
4 x facilitator gloves- 3 x magic gloves, 1 x fur trimmed leather gloves
Lightning bolt
MISS CACKLE table - with the cups and saucers
MISS CACKLE chair
MISS CACKLE stool

Under props table:
ENID's suit bag
ENID's gym ribbon
ENID's cat basket
ENID's vanity case
AGATHA framed picture

STAGE RIGHT
Rosin

US of 2nd masker:
- Drusilla suitcase (grey and black) and cat basket- with striped collar cat, and black body inside
- Fenella suitcase (butterfly) and cat basket- with yellow / red collar cat, and black body inside

MISS BAT *music stand:*
- Open music book
- Spare Mother moon score tucked into pages of music book
- 6 x mother moon scores on L-H side of book
- 2 x flying cats (2 x tails and 2 x gloves) over back of stand
- 1 x Tabby glove. L-H. and 1 x sleeve (Becky) on R-H side of book

ETHEL's *potions desk:*
- Set with all potions items
- Tail, pig nose and pig ears in cupboard

2 x standard brooms
Breakable broom
Enid's broomstick carrier
Enid's witch hat box
Enid's PS4 box
6 x exercise books
5 x spell books

Water bottle caddy:
- With first aid kit, silver foil blanket folded into side
- 3 x bottles filled with water
- Pendant

1 x facilitator glove
3 x Nightstars
Tabby body
Dragonsbane
3 x lanterns
Snail antennae
2 x picture frames with mounts
Tea tray with 2 x cups and saucers, teapot and plate of buns

Under props table:
Snail shell
Tabby cat basket
1 x Tabby glove.

US of props table:
5 x student cloaks (Maud, Fenella, Ethel, Drusilla, Mildred.
WARDROBE)
Crash mat
Act 2 crumpets and buns

ACT 1 - PERSONALS

MISS BAT
Conducting baton in hair
Miss Bat tea cup and saucer

MISS DRILL
Miss Drill's whistle

ACT 2

PRESET ONSTAGE
Curtains closed
Set in position 1 (red)
Mountain in
Mirror on. Sunglasses in drawer
Trunk open with blue cloak draped over edge

MUSIC CORNER
Enid mic
Tabby glove on shelf.

DORMITORY PLATFORM
STRIKE exercise books
2 x Nightstars on bed. TURN ON. Left hand underneath

MISS CACKLE'S OFFICE
Chair and stool against potion shelves
Witches Code on shelf

ON STAIRS TO MISS CACKLE'S OFFICE
Half and half wig on wig stand

BEHIND BACKCLOTH
Ladders and tallescope

STAGE LEFT
Scooter
2 x standard brooms
MILDRED whole broom
Trunk Mirror and cloaks inside
  - Witches' code
  - Head girl badge
Door knob
Clipboard with pencil

Comms headset and pack
MAUD glasses
2 x band water bottles (Clean and full of drinking water.)
1 x tabby glove.
1 x tabby sleeve.
Small snail

Cat collection point:
   - **MILDRED** sleeve and glove (R-H)
   - **MAUD** sleeve and glove (R-H)
   - **ENID** sleeve and glove (R-H)
Lightning bolt
Miss Cackle table – with the cups and saucers

STAGE RIGHT
3 x standard brooms
Desk
Pendant
4 x Nightstars
Dragonsbane
3 x lanterns
Snail antennae
2 x picture frames with mounts
Tea tray with 2 x cups and saucers, teapot and plate of iced buns with cherries
Plate of crumpets

Under props table
Snail shell

ACT 2 - PERSONALS

MISS BAT
Conducting baton in hair

MISS DRILL
Miss Drill's whistle

PUPPET PARTS

TABBIES

FENELLA (F) – 1 x glove (striped)

DRUSILLA (D) – 1 x glove (R–H, plain); 1 x sleeve; 2 x feet (double width); 2 x feet with elastic knots (NOT USED)

ETHEL (Eth) – 1 x glove (L–H, striped). NOT USED

MILDRED (Mil) – 3 x glove (2 x R–H, 1 x L–H, plain) 2 x sleeves

MAUD (Ma) – 2 x gloves (pair, plain); 1 x sleeve; 2 x feet

ENID (En) – 2 x gloves (pair, plain); 1 x sleeve

MISS CACKLE (MissC) – 1 x glove (R–H, striped); 1 x sleeve

1 x whole Tabby body

NIGHTSTARS

6 x Nightstar (2 x **ENID** – both compression switch, 1 x **ETHEL** – compression switch, 1 x **MISS DRILL** on/off, 1 x **ENID** – on/off, 1 x **MISS HARDBROOM** on/off)

FLYING CATS

2 x tails (**MILDRED** and **MAUD**)

2 x black gloves (**ETHEL** and **DRUSILLA**)

CAT BASKETS

4 x sewn glove and sleeves (**DRUSILLA** – coloured stripes, **ETHEL** – Nightstar. NO LEDs, **FENELLA** – yellow/red, **MAUD** – blue collar)

4 x black cat bodies

VISIT THE SAMUEL FRENCH BOOKSHOP AT THE ROYAL COURT THEATRE

Browse plays and theatre books, get expert advice and enjoy a coffee

Samuel French Bookshop
Royal Court Theatre
Sloane Square
London
SW1W 8AS
020 7565 5024

Shop from thousands of titles on our website

 samuelfrench.co.uk

 samuelfrenchltd

 samuel french uk

Lightning Source UK Ltd.
Milton Keynes UK
UKHW011334010419
340279UK00005B/341/P